❧❦❧

The Ups and Downs
of Life

The Ups and Downs of Life

Captain Edward Sellon

WORDSWORTH CLASSICS

The Ups & Downs of Life was first published by Wm Dugdale
(London, 1867). It was reprinted by Auguste Brancart (Brussels, 1892) as *The Amorous Prowess of a Jolly Fellow or His
Adventures with Lovely Girls as Related by Himself*. The text of the
present edition is an edited version of the previous two
printings, correcting misspellings and obvious grammatical and
syntactical errors found in those editions,
This text is copyright © 1987 by Dennis R. McMillan and
Clifford J. Scheiner, and no part of it may be reproduced
without the written permission of the publishers

Introduction and Postscript copyright © 1987 by C. J. Scheiner

This edition published 1996 by
Wordsworth Editions Limited
Cumberland House, Crib Street
Ware, Hertfordshire SG12 9ET

ISBN 1 85326 629 9

This edition © Wordsworth Editions Limited 1996

Typeset by Antony Gray
Printed and bound in Great Britain by
Mackays of Chatham plc, Chatham, Kent

❧ *Introduction* ❧
to the 1987 American edition

The Ups and Downs of Life by Captain Edward Sellon is the rarest erotic autobiography known. Years of searching by professional bookscouts and collectors in the genre have produced only a single extant copy of the 1867 first edition, and that book presently resides in a private collection, inaccessible to the general public. (Ironically, the only other known printed copy of the text, from a small edition published in Brussels in 1892, is in the very same private library and it is only through the cooperation and friendship of the current owner of the two volumes that this modern reprint of *The Ups and Downs of Life* has been made possible.)

Rarity alone is not a sufficient justification for reprinting any given work of prose. The text must be judged informative, entertaining, and of interest to at least enough students or *aficionados* of the genre at large to justify the costs involved in producing a high-quality book in a relatively small number of copies. Sellon's erotic autobiography qualifies on all counts. His first-hand experience as a soldier in colonial India, where he was a student of Hindu and Tamil social and sexual customs, combined with his experiences as a 'Victorian gentleman' and his uninhibited libertinism and totally candid honesty, give us a nonpareil view of the sexual mores of his times (1818–66).

A quick summary of Sellon's life is in order, although one cannot do better than the autobiography of the subject himself. What we know of Sellon comes mostly from this autobiography, with additional commentary from the writings of his good friend, Henry Spencer Ashbee, and portions of the other prose, verse, art and letters that he left behind. Born in 1818 to a moderately well-off English family, his father died when he was still a child and his upbringing (and much of his adult life as well) was under the influence of his strong-willed mother. Edward received a good education, strong in upper-school subjects such as languages and the classics. At age sixteen he was sent out to India as a military cadet, and by the end of a ten-year tour had achieved the rank of captain. In 1844 he returned to England to a marriage arranged by his mother, which quickly collapsed when he found his new bride not as wealthy as she had represented herself to be. The balance of his marital life was stormy, with frequent fights and separations and reconciliations, all complicated by financial reverses and Sellon's innumerable infidelities. Even the birth of a son could not quell his penchant for a rake's life and he supported himself over the later years of his life as a stage driver, fencing master and writer/illustrator of pornographic literature. In April 1866, at the age of forty-eight, he committed suicide in Webb's Hotel, Picadilly, London. He died from a self-inflicted gunshot wound.

Edward Sellon's life was relatively brief, but contained more adventures than most men would experience in several full lifetimes. He was educated and multi-talented. He was also completely sexually amoral (although he evidently did follow his own code of ethics in other areas of intercourse with his fellow [wo]man), and apparently also fearless to the point of foolhardiness. He gave not a wit for the conventional social code; not that he was a vicious sinner out to harm his fellow man – he just could not pass up a good time, regardless of the consequences. Sellon's life was complicated greatly by his

6

fondness for young girls, a taste no doubt acquired in India, where paedophilia was quite prevalent and more liberally tolerated than in England. Brought back to the land of his birth, it proved to be a scourge that led him into increasingly outrageous behaviour, finally resulting in a grand scandal and his being ostracized from 'polite society' (an incident described in detail in the present volume). Like the *carp diem* courtiers of the court of Charles II two centuries before, he was a consumate *roué*. (As such he might well be compared to John Wilmot, the Earl of Rochester, who was the boon companion of Charles II, and was author of several notorious pornographic pieces, including the obscene play *Sodom*.)

It is no wonder that this man lived perpetually in the sexual *sub rosa* of his society. He could write knowledgeably about such topics as prostitution, sex worship, marital infidelity, erotic art and literature and minority sexual practices, because these were all common areas of his life. What is important to us is not that Captain Edward Sellon studied and participated in these debaucheries, but that he accurately and honestly recorded them for posterity In his autobiography he is completely candid. He does not apologize for his indiscretions, nor does he falsify his activities to present himself in a better light. *The Ups and Downs of Life* is a frank record of Victorian sexuality and socio-sexual mores, written contemporarily with the actual incidents, from first-hand knowledge, and in the language and argot of the day.

The Ups and Downs of Life is a simple narrative, written in a lucid, syntactically competent, fast-paced style, making for exciting reading. Sellon can tell a good tale, and he does; he grabs his reader's attention and keeps it. He spares euphemism and reports his escapades, erotic and otherwise, with almost journalistic precision. The stated purpose of *The Ups and Downs of Life* is to present the author's 'erotic autobiography', and as such it succeeds magnificently. Along with scenes of frantic sexual activity (including a comic transvestite incident starring himself), Sellon gives personal insights into the details that surrounded his sexual life and maturation during the first two thirds of the nineteenth century. It is through him that we can obtain an accurate description of the social evils of the time, be it the daily workings of English harlotry, the sexual exploitation of the young in England and India, child prostitution, the sexual customs of English colonial troops, or the sorry state of Victorian marital fidelity – clearly shown to be grounded in the nearly total economic dependence of women on men (often much older than themselves, and to whom they were married by their families for financial concerns only). Here is primary material for the historian, sociologist, psychologist and feminist, as well as the curious reader at large. The linguist will find the language of the book rich in slang – the general argot of the day, the cant of army life, and the specialised Hindu and Tamil dialects and bastardised English that came to be used by both the English army and their servants in colonial India.

One might well question whether Sellon's record is accurate and honest. Based on the letters he wrote and the other semi-autobiographical works he produced, a consistency is noted with what we are told in *The Ups and Downs of Life*, and the accounts of people who knew him, such as H. S. Ashbee, indicate that the descriptions presented are true to his character and activities.

A fuller picture of Edward Sellon may emerge from a review of the various works he authored. Most appeared during the last few years of his life, at a time when he was desperately in need of money. His writings can be most easily grouped as:

1. non-erotic fiction
2. ethnosexological works
3. translations
4. erotic fiction
5. erotic art

Here is a list of works for which Edward Sellon has received credit:

1. *Herbert Breakspeare. A Legend of the Mahratta War* (London, Whittaker and Co., Ave Maria Lane, and sold by A. Wallis and R. Folthrop, Brighton, 1848)

   A non-erotic adventure novel based on Sellon's life in India in the colonial army. H. S. Ashbee, in his *Catena Librorum Tacendorum*, quotes and comments as follows on the book:

   'For the delineation of native character, manners, and costume, I have relied almost solely on my own observations, during a residence in India of nearly six years,' observes the author in his dedication, and it must be confessed that *Herbert Breakspeare*, although perhaps a somewhat jejune performance, possesses, apart from the interest of the narrative itself, sufficient *couleur locale* to entitle it to a certain consideration. It contains the adventures, for the most part in India, of the two cousins – Herbert Breakspeare, brave, honest, open-hearted, a perfect gentleman, and Everhard [! – Ed.], a heartless, disloyal scamp, whose aim is to supplant the confiding Herbert in the affection of both his father and his bride. Everhard is betrayed by a native girl, whom he had abandoned, into the hands of a Mahratta chief, into whose court he had penetrated as a spy, and is executed. Herbert, on the other hand, although wounded in an engagement with the enemy, is saved through the greatful generosity of a Mahratta, whose life he had on a previous occasion preserved. He returns home to wed the girl of his love, and solace the declining years of a doting father.

It might be noted that the two main protagonists seem to represent the conflicting alter-egos of which Captain Sellon was composed.

2a *Annotations on the Sacred Writings of the Hindus* (London, 1865; privately printed)

A treatise on Indian sex beliefs and practices, based on first-hand research, that is still a classic book on the subject. It placed Sellon in the ranks of such other Victorian ethnographers as Sir Richard Burton.

2b 'On Lingua Puja, or Phallic Worship of India'. A paper read before the Anthropological Society in January 1865.

2c 'Some Remarks on the Sancti Puja or the Worship of the Female Powers', 1866. A paper for presentation to the Anthropological Society.

2d *The Monolithic Temples of India* (*c.*1865)

3a *Selections from the Decameron of Giovanni Boccaccio. Including all the Passages hitherto Suppressed* (London, 1865)
Translated from the Italian by Sellon.

3b *Gita-Radhica-Khrishna. A Sanskrit Poem* (*c.*1865)
Sellon edited the English translation of this epic.

3c *The Index Expurgatorious of Martial* (London, 1868)
A translation from the Latin of the more socially unacceptable epigrams of the classic Roman author. The work was done in conjunction with, among others, George Augusta Sala and F. P. Pike.

4a *The New Epicurean* (London, Wm Dugdale, 1865)
A somewhat autobiographical erotic novel that reworks many of his Indian and paedophilic experiences into an English country setting.

4b. *Phoebe Kissagen* (London, Wm Dugdale, 1866)
A continuation of *The New Epicurean*.

4c *Adventures of a Gentleman* (*c.* 1865)
An unpublished manuscript which is noted by Ashbee (*Catena*, p. 427). The contents of this tale are unknown, and the mss. is conjectured by Ashbee to have been destroyed.

4d. *Scenes in the Life of a Young Man* (*c.* 1865)
An erotic tale that was to be included with *Phoebe Kissagen*, but which was apparently never printed.

4e. 'The Confessions of a Single Man' (*c.* 1865)
An unpublished short erotic story.

4f. 'The Delights of Imagination'
An unpublished erotic short story.

4g *Cythera's Hymnal* (London, 1870)
A collection of erotic verse and parodies, popular among college students of the time, in part gathered by Sellon, who also authored at least two of the pieces: 'No More' and 'Chordee'.

4h *The New Ladies' Tickler* (London, 1866)
Ashbee attributes only the art to Sellon, but others, such as Dawes, credit Sellon with the text also. However, as the book contains numerous flagellation scenes, it is doubtful that Sellon penned it, or at least those parts.

4i *The Adventures of a School Boy* (London, 1866)
Although Ashbee indicates that Sellon only contributed the illustrations for this erotic novel (and in a note in his own copy of his Index indicates J.C. Reddie to be the author of

the work), based on the style, language and themes, several authorities, such as C.R. Dawes, believe the text to have been penned by Sellon as well.

5 Illustrations
Ashbee reports that Edward Sellon illustrated many of his own books, including *The Ups and Downs of Life*, *The New Epicurean*, *Phoebe Kissagen*, *Adventures of a Gentleman*, and also did illustrations (at the request of the publisher, Wm Dugdale) for *The Adventures of a School Boy*, *The New Ladies' Tickler*, *The Amorous Quaker* and *Memoirs of Rosa Bellefille*. At his death there were many other erotic illustrations remaining that had yet to be used.

The previous publishing history of Edward Sellon's *The Ups and Downs of Life* is brief. The manuscript for this erotic autobiography was left unfinished at the time of the author's death. The work had already been sold to the London pornography publisher Wm Dugdale, for whom Sellon had previously written and illustrated several erotic works. Sellon had made sixteen coloured drawings, a coloured title page, and two pen-and-ink drawings to accompany the text, as well as a fancy pen-and-ink title. Dugdale chose eight of these to be made up in lithograph to accompany his first edition of the book, which appeared in 1867, and consisted of 110 pages of text, to which he appended a note concerning the abruptness of the ending of the book (Ashbee comments that the final note was written by Sellon himself). The second edition of the book appeared in 1892, published in Brussels by Auguste Brancart, who issued the text under the new title of *The Amorous Prowess of a Jolly Fellow or His Adventures with Lovely Girls Related by*

Himself. This edition consisted of 137 pages and no illustrations. A French translation of *The Ups and Downs of Life*, announced for publication in 1891, apparently never appeared.

The current edition of Captain Edward Sellon's erotic autobiography reproduces the illustrations from the unique extant volume of the first edition, and utilises the texts from the 1867 and 1892 editions. The text has been edited to correct obvious misspellings and some evident grammatical and syntactical lapses of past publishers and printers. To make the present edition more useful to modern readers, a glossary has been appended at the end of the text to elucidate some of the more unfamiliar or archaic words and phrases.

The present publishers are pleased to present, for the first time in nearly a century, a most interesting look deep into the sexual mores of early-nineteenth-century English life. The author was a 'sinner' of the highest degree, and this sad man paid for his indiscretions all too dearly by social ostracisation and an early death by his own hand. Yet, in his candour, he has done posterity a great service, for he has told us what the Victorian censors laboured to hide – the truth. Through Edward Sellon's works we have a more complete and honest perspective on a period of history known for its strict public morality and ultimate hypocrisy.

C. J. SCHEINER
Brooklyn, NY
September 1987

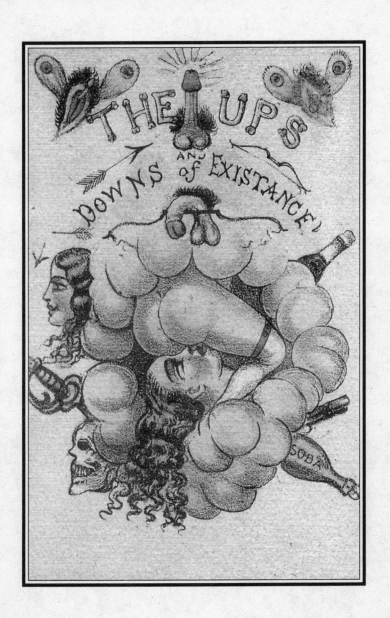

THE UPS

AND

DOWNS of EXISTANCE

All the world's a stage,
And all the men and women merely players;
They have their exits and their entrances,
And one man in his time plays many parts.

As You Like It, ACT 2, SCENE VII

❦ I ❧

Showing how I commenced my career in the Court of Venus

The son of a gentleman of moderate fortune, whom I lost when quite a child, I was designed from the first for the army. Having, at the age of sixteen, been presented with a cadetship, so soon as my outfit was completed, I started by the mail for Portsmouth, on a cold night in February 1834. Arrived at Portsmouth, I put up at the Fountain Inn, the George being full, and the next day called at the latter hotel to pay my respects and present a letter of introduction to Major S—, who, with his three nieces and daughter, was there staying.

I found the old major discussing a bottle of port, in spite of his gout, and he gave me hearty reception. He was a specimen of the old school of company's officers, of which few now remain. Bluff, hearty and hospitable, he was a man of some sixty years of age, who had seen some hard service in his youth. But poverty, that bane of human life, forbade his enjoying his *otium cum dignitate*. In fact, he was again returning to India in search of his colonelcy, which promotion yet tarried.

'Well, youngster,' said he, 'so you're going to try your fortune in India, eh? you won't find the Pagodas grow on the trees now, my lad, the golden fruit has been plucked long ago; but you seem a likely young chap, so I drink to your success, here's to you, my

17

boy,' and he swallowed a bumper, pushing the bottle at the same time to me. I tippled and talked, for I was not troubled with *mauvaise honte* even at sixteen, and at eight o'clock I rose to take leave. 'Well, my lad, good-night,' said the old major, 'and harkee, the skipper tells me that we are likely to be detained here for a week or two by this cursed south-west gale, so you had better come and take up your quarters with me at Southsea, where I have taken lodgings – 22 Portsea Terrace – come tomorrow and I'll introduce you to my nieces!' At the words nieces I pricked up my ears, and promising to come, I took leave and returned to the Fountain. I went into the coffee-room and, in the grand way known only to griffins, called loudly for a pint of wine and some filberts. The boxes were all occupied, and as I sought for a table, a fine, handsome fellow who was languidly drinking a bottle of claret, accosted me. 'Here's room, take a seat here, glad of your company.' I bowed carelessly, for I had been so used to meet good society at my uncle's, that I had none of the schoolboy shyness which is usual with beardless boys of sixteen. I did not notice it then, but I have since thought my quondam acquaintance must have been immensely amused with me.

When the waiter brought my 'stingy port', he passed his claret to me, saying, 'Don't drink that stuff, try this, 'tis real Château Margaux, by God, try it.'

I sipped a glass and made a wry face, 'Thank you,' said I, 'I'd rather stick to my stingo.' He shrugged his shoulders, but said nothing, so I went on with my port. My new friend then informed me that he belonged to the British Legion, under Sir De Lacy Evans, and was pledged to the cause of Don Pedro, and was, like me, waiting for a fair wind to sail to Portugal. Of course, I reciprocated his confidence by telling him that I was going to India as a cadet.

As soon as we had both finished our wine, he pulled out a cigar-case and lit a real Havannah, a rarity in those non-smoking days, then he offered me his case. I was wonderfully fascinated with this man – his handsome person, black moustache turned up *à la* Carolus 1st, and dashing air quite captivated me.

'What are you going to do tonight?' said he.

'Damme!' said I, hazarding my first oath, 'I'm game for anything.'

'Suppose we go to the theatre?' said he.

'With all my heart,' said I.

So to the theatre we went. On the way he told me his various adventures with the girls at Portsmouth and cautioned me against them. But on coming out of the theatre we were surrounded by a bevy of blooming loves (at least if their cheeks were not blooming, the paint was), and my guardian friend was quickly carried off. As for me, I remained like a lamb doomed to the slaughter; a bold devil about five-and-twenty had seized me and was about to make me her prey, when she was swooped down upon by a pretty little creature of fifteen, who in peremptory language desired her to loose her hold. What influence the young girl had upon the older one I don't know, but she obeyed without a word, and the other taking my arm led me away.

'You are a little cadet,' she said, 'I know, and a very pretty boy you are, and shall come and sleep with me!' I turned my eyes on my captor, she was very pretty and I yielded at discretion.

She led me through a number of horrid dark streets and at length stopped before a grim-looking door. Three peculiar raps procured instant admission. Following my conductor, I stumbled up the worm-eaten stairs; she drew a key from her pocket and opened a door. I was almost blinded by the blaze of light that met my eyes. A sumptuous room containing every elegancy of life was before me; upon a console table was set out a cold collation. Champagne stood in ice. Two little girls, naked as the day they were born, came forward to do the honours. The room was as hot as July, owing to the two tremendous fires that blazed in the apartments.

'You haven't a five-pound note about you, my dear boy?' said the siren.

'I have two,' said I, innocently enough.

'Oh! you little darling!' said the pretty creature and my purse was emptied in an instant.

'Come along, darling!' said the girl, 'have some supper.'

In those halcyon days my appetite was good, my stomach was iron, my head was brass, I ate, I drank, God! how I quaffed the champagne.

'Well, I'm damned!' said Polly (for that was her name), 'by God, you're a little trump,' and she flung herself on a sofa and tossed up her clothes. I sprang towards her. 'Oh, you dear little boy,' said she, 'let me look at the pretty little cock; is it a virgin?' and she took it in her mouth. I was in raptures and seized on her beauteous cunt. I kissed her breasts, I mounted her and crack went my frenum in an instant. Oh, ye who have not wasted your early vigour in riotous frigging, tell me, was ever in your after days any joy like that first delicious fuck? Talk of heaven! talk of the bliss 'which it hath not entered the heart of man to conceive'!

> Oh, the world are all thinking about it,
> And as for myself I can swear,
> If I fancied that heaven were without it,
> I'd scarce feel a wish to go there!

Heaven can't be finer, and so I found it. I fucked Polly four times, the little girls twice a-piece, I drank two bottles of champagne and returned to my hotel at five in the morning, with my prick as raw as a carrot 'tis true, but sober as a parson. At ten o'clock I had breakfasted and was on my way to Portsea Terrace, fresh and lively as a lark. Oh, those youthful days! those dear, darling, youthful days! had I three hundred thousand a year, I would gladly give a moiety of my income for their return.

Ave! Polly! dear destroyer of my virginity! where art thou now? Alas, alas! poxed! used up! dead, perhaps; or, sad alternative! perhaps, grown old, stale and shrivelled, you sell oranges at the corners of streets, or sweep a dirty crossing. *Telle est la vie!* – such is life!

I never saw her again, for at Portsea Terrace I found I had 'other fish to fry' – now isn't that vulgar? What an expression amidst such Aphrodisiac rhapsodies. All right, old fellow, but you know 'there is but one step from the sublime to the ridiculous'.

Arrived at Portsea Terrace, I was at once introduced to the nieces of Major — They were three in number: Henrietta, a fine girl of two-and-twenty, with dark brown eyes and skin of pure white and red; Lucy, aged eighteen, a sparkling brunette with a lovely figure and almond-shaped eyes; and Fanny, also a dark beauty of fourteen, but so developed, she looked five-and-twenty at least. As for the good major's wife, she was old and fat and his daughter plain and scraggy. But there were two other young ladies going out to Madras under his care, who I suppose would have been considered fine women, the Misses N—l, but they did not particularly take my fancy.

A pretty, rosy, laughing little chambermaid showed me my room when it was time to go to bed and, simpering as she set down the candle, said, 'Do not be alarmed if you hear a noise in the night, sir. Captain Fraser, of the *Azincour*, occupies the next room with his wife and he comes in late sometimes and a little the worse for liquor.'

I glanced at the folding-doors against which the head of my bed stood and naïvely remarked, 'Well, if I hear them quarrel, I shall also hear them make love!'

'Oh, fie!' said the girl, with an arch look.

'Heigh, ho!' said I, 'I wish I had a bedfellow too, it is so cold!'

'Do you really though, dear?' said the pretty creature, looking, as I thought, rather lovingly at me.

'Indeed, I do and I could not wish for a prettier one than you!'

'Oh you saucy little man!' cried the girl, giving me a playful slap on the face which did not hurt the least. 'Why you are a mere boy.'

'Come and sleep with me,' said I, 'and I will show you I can act like a man.'

I slipped five shillings into her hand and gave her a kiss.

'But,' said she, hesitatingly, 'if my missus should find it out – if you were to get me with child?'

'Oh! no fear of that, my pet, I'm too young for that, but I think you could please me and I'm sure I could please you.'

'Well, look here, dear,' said the girl, 'my missus will go to bed in about an hour and then I will come.'

I hugged her in my arms and, as an earnest of what I was to have, she let me feel her little cunny, on which a few hairs were beginning to sprout.

What a long hour of expectation it was and how I tossed and tumbled in the bed, but at length the happy moment arrived. I heard the door open softly and Mary appeared in her shift, shading the light with her hand. She was going to put it out, but I stopped her, bade her lock the door and come at once to bed. She obeyed with the greatest docility. Then I had her shift up in an instant and covered every part of her white body with kisses. The next moment I was between her thighs and slipped into her spending cunny without any difficulty. How I buried my face between those breasts of snow! how I slapped those thighs! what a frantic fuck it was. When it was over I whispered, 'Ah, then, this is not your first time?'

'Nor your's, dear boy!' she replied, hugging me.

'Nor mine,' I ejaculated, returning the embrace.

'Why, how old are you?' said Mary.

'Sixteen last month,' I replied. And you?'

'Well, I'm not sixteen yet, but shall be in March.'

'The devil!' I exclaimed, 'and how many men have you had?'

'Let me see,' said Mary, thinking, 'well, about fifteen, I fancy.'

'Oh, then, you know all about it?'

'Pretty well,' said she.

By this I was ready again and was going to work *en règle*, but she stopped me. 'I'll show you another way for a change, which a ship's captain, who was lodging here, taught me, and I think you will like it,' and kneeling upon all fours, she told me to kneel behind her. Now it had never before occurred to me that there could be anything attractive in the hinder beauties of a woman; I had been accustomed to look in front.

But, oh ye gods and little fishes! what a new and enchanting delight thrilled through all my veins as those bulging hips, those dimpled white hemispheres arose on my view. I stooped down and imprinted a loving kiss on each lovely globe, and then grasping her ivory thighs, I drove into her mossy grotto, wondering in my mind why nature had placed it so near another and not so savoury aperture! I moved with frenzy, she toyed with the balls of love! Was ever young mortal so blessed? Happy, thrice happy, golden days of fiery youth. Our climax came! I took no heed of it. Without a descent, I commenced again and at length fell fainting on her alabaster back. Then rolling over on the bed with Mary clasped to my breast, my lips glued to hers, her tongue in my mouth, I fell into a delicious slumber. How long we lay sleeping I know not, but I was awakened by a gruff voice in the next room, which seemed to be craving some favour which his female companion appeared not inclined to grant.

'What does the fellow want to do, Mary?' I whispered.

'Hush!' said she, stopping my mouth with a kiss. 'Listen and you will hear. He's a damned old beast and behaves shamefully to his poor little wife.'

'Mrs Fraser?' said I, interrogatively.

'Yes,' she whispered, 'she is only eighteen, beautiful as an angel and so sweet tempered, yet I believe he has not yet taken her virginity, and they have been married a month, and he is forty at least.'

'You surprise me,' said I, 'for what did he marry her then?'

'Oh! you will hear presently if you'll only listen instead of talking so, naughty boy!'

I was silent.

Captain Fraser: 'Come, my darling, do kneel up, there's a dear, I want to see your peach-like bottom.'

Mrs Fraser: 'Oh, pray don't, Harry, it is so big! and you do hurt that poor little place so! do put it in the other, that is meant for it, I'm sure! pray do!'

Captain Fraser: 'Nonsense, my dear, I prefer the smaller hole, now don't be foolish; kneel up!'

Mrs Fraser: 'Oh, Harry, pray don't. I'm quite sore with what you did last night; pray do go to sleep if you can't do it in the right place!'

Captain Fraser: 'God damn your eyes! if you don't kneel up at once, I'll pinch you black and blue, and I'll beat you.'

Mrs Fraser, crying: 'Ah! Harry, you are a cruel man; it was not for this that I married you.'

Captain Fraser: 'Will you kneel up?'

A rustling of bedclothes and a shaking of the bedstead proclaimed that the poor little wife had complied.

'Let us look at them,' whispered Mary, drawing me out of bed; she pulled a knot out of the folding-doors, and we had a full view of the next apartment. Kneeling up on her hands and knees was one of the most beautiful young women I had ever beheld. She was entirely naked; behind her knelt a great, ugly brute of a man, whose bleared eyes showed him half drunk, and whose thick grizzled black whiskers and scowling brows formed a strange contrast to the angelic creature prostrate before him. 'Beauty and the beast!' I whispered to Mary, but she put her hand before my mouth.

Mrs Fraser: 'Oh, God! oh! oh! Harry, you hurt me cruel!'

Captain Fraser: 'Therein lies my pleasure, my pretty boy! oh! your bottom is just like the lovely boy's. Ah! now I see my cock entering your anus! It is distended to the utmost; now I am in! further! oh, bliss!'

Mrs Fraser: 'Oh! my God, what torment. Oh! cru–el ma–n, stop, ah! oh! you will destroy me; oh!' and she sank on the bed and sobbed as if her heart would break.

'Damn it,' I cried, 'I can't stand this, that old scoundrel ought to be taken out and shot!'

Mary stood looking at me petrified with terror, for I had uttered this aloud, then flying to the door she made her escape.

The captain drew out in an instant and looked towards the folding doors like a man bereft of his senses, his face pale as death, his lips twitching with nervous anxiety. He had heard my exclamation. I watched him as he dressed himself quickly and taking no notice of his young wife, who lay moaning on the bed, put on his hat and fled.

I heard him go down the stairs, I heard him unbar the front door, I heard him bang it after him and I had no more doubt in my mind that he had gone at once on board his ship, and that before day dawned he would be beating down channel in the *Azincour*, spite of the sou'wester in his teeth, than if I had followed in his wake and seen him. But convinced though I was that such would be the case, I was sufficiently prudent to go downstairs and bar and bolt the front door in case my gentleman should have a latchkey and return. This done, I went upstairs, but instead of returning to my own room, went boldly into his.

Mrs Fraser started up at my entrance, supposing it had been her lord – but seeing nothing but a rosy little boy she said, gently enough – 'My dear, you have mistaken your room, Captain Fraser, my husband, and I sleep here.'

I advanced, and sitting down on her bed, thus addressed her: 'My dear, Mrs Fraser, I am quite aware that this is not my room. I occupy the next apartment, and in occupying it both heard and saw all that passed between you and that miscreant your husband. 'Twas I who made the exclamation which caused him to flee this house, and he is now, I have no doubt, making the best of his way on board his ship, and will be beating down channel in a few hours, spite of the gale. But suppose he should not sail, should return, he cannot get in here tonight; the people of the house are gone to bed, and I have bolted and barred the front door.'

Poor Mrs Fraser sat up in the bed and regarded me attentively, 'To look at you, one would think you a child,' she said, 'but you talk like a man!'

'I am so much a man, my dear Mrs Fraser, that I would have poignarded that scoundrel just now, had I been near him; but as I cannot wound his body, I am here to wound his honour, if indeed he has any to lose. Take me in your arms, dearest girl, and I will soon show you what he ought to have done, and what blisses you have lost by marrying such as him.'

I sprang into the bed and clasped her in my arms; she leant her head on my shoulder and sobbed. At that moment, if the redoubtable Captain Fraser had appeared armed to the teeth, I believe I could have given him battle and conquered. God! how I loved, how I pitied that woman – 'I hope,' I said, 'he has not done you any "irretrievable injury".'

'He ruptured me the first night,' she sobbed out, 'and since then I have endured nothing but torment. Ah! how I loved him, and what a fond wife I could have been!'

'You break my heart,' said I. 'I was going to make the offer of my person to you, but by God, you disarm me, I am wretched.'

'Sweetest, sweetest boy,' she said, 'I love him no longer, come to my arms and teach me, though you be so young, what a wife ought to know. I abandon myself to your dear embrace, and God forgive me if I am wrong, but I have been cruelly victimised by him who ought to have been my protector.'

I embraced my fair creature with rapture, and was soon in

possession of her hitherto despised maidenhead.

'I care not for this pain, darling boy,' she said, 'it is a natural legitimate pain, and I only love you for inflicting it, but before you begin again do look and see how that brute has injured me!' and she knelt up, jutting out her heavenly bottom, showed me her poor little anus all inflamed, distended and torn, bleeding, absolutely bleeding. 'It was cruel of him, was it not?' she said, 'to treat me so barbarously?'

'Poor darling!' I exclaimed. 'It is most shameful indeed, poor dear love!'

Then suffering her to guide my stiffened prick to the right entrance, I and she were soon again lost in bliss. Morning and Mary found us locked in each other's arms.

Dear little Mary, what a reproachful glance she cast upon me. But I quieted her with a gesture, and drawing her towards me, whispered, 'I could do no less, my angel; go, take a sovereign out of my purse, you will find it on the dressing-table, and say nothing of what you have seen.' She kissed me passionately and withdrew.

Then I turned to the pretty creature by my side, and casting my arms around her neck, wooed her to a matutinal embrace. She responded instantly, and mounting over me, took the active part, while I toyed with her full and enchanting breasts. When this was over, we mutually compared notes as to our future proceedings. She told me that she could not endure that we should part when the ship sailed, in which my passage was taken, and that she had thought of a plan by which we should still be together. Captain Fraser had kept her very short of money, and as he was bound to Madras, Singapore and China, he might not be back for years. She did not care about returning to her home, as her family had always treated her harshly. She, therefore, intended to ask Captain A—l, of the *Reliance*, to take her as stewardess, 'and then you know, dearest boy, you can slip into my cabin sometimes'. I thanked her with a kiss, and approved of her plan. I offered her ten pounds in case she should not have enough money to pay her lodging bill, but she declined it, saying she had enough by her to meet that charge, and had also a pretty good outfit.

So that matter settled, I bid her goodbye for the present, and went to my own room to dress.

At breakfast I was abstracted and taciturn, spite of the blandishments of the young ladies, for I was anxious to go down to the Sallyport, and find out if Captain Fraser had sailed. So making some excuse about seeing if Messrs Grindley & Co. had sent my luggage from London, I put on my hat and made the best of my way to the Hard. Here I soon learnt that Captain Fraser had come down there at midnight, and to the great astonishment of the few watermen that yet lingered in hope of a fare, had gone on board; that the *Azincour* had immediately weighed anchor, and stood out to sea in the teeth of the remonstrances of the pilot and the manifest discontent of the crew.

I returned quite elated with the news, and sent a little pencil note up to Mrs Fraser. I now proposed a walk to the young ladies. Lucy and Miss N—l accepted my escort, but the others, having some letters to write, stayed at home.

I made myself as agreeable as I could, and proposed that we should go over to Ryde in the steamer, see what we could of the Isle of Wight, lunch there, and get back to Southsea in time to dress for our six o'clock dinner. The girls clapped their hands and declared that would be capital fun, and away we went. It was a fine day, though the wind blew a hard gale from the sou'-sou'-west, which did not incommode me in the least, and only showed off to advantage the fine shape of my companions, for there were no odious crinolines in those days.

As soon as we landed at Ryde we made the best of our way out of that ugly town, with its prim red-brick houses, and soon found ourselves scrambling amidst the woods in the neighbourhood.

The girls got very skittish, climbing trees, and playing all sorts of pranks, giving me abundance of opportunities of seeing all their beauties, which were of the most *recherché* description.

Lucy, catching me peeping, made great pretence of concealing what it was evident she meant to show, exclaiming, 'Now! what are you looking at, naughty boy! for shame! Louisa, take care! you are showing your legs tremendously; the young rogue will see you, too, I declare,' etc.

All this seemed to me very funny, so I thought I would play them a trick. I proposed that we should have a game of hide and seek, and I offered to go and hide; this was agreed to, and they came scrambling out of the trees.

'Now,' I said, 'hide your eyes and don't stir till I cry whoop!' I dashed off as if intending to go some distance, but presently doubled and returned to within a yard of them, concealing myself in a hollow oak. Just as I turned to double, I cried, 'whoop!' so hearing my voice at some distance, they had no idea that I was so near. They were engaged in an animated conversation, the end of which reached my ears as they darted off.

Lucy was saying, 'Yes, he is a mere boy to look at, but I'm very much mistaken if those dark eyes don't mean mischief – did you see how they sparkled when we showed our thighs? Oh, he'll do, Louisa, he'll do!' and off they ran.

I very readily understood the meaning of the amorous Lucy, so drawing out my ivory truncheon, I removed behind the tree, placing myself in an attitude which seemed to imply that I was performing a lustration of its roots. Then I shouted out twice in succession, 'whoop, whoop!' They soon appeared, running full tilt at the tree.

'Stop, stop a moment!' I shouted, with an affectation of modesty I was far from feeling. But they only came on the faster, one ran one side of the oak, the other the other side, so that simultaneously they had a clear full view of that manly attribute which set at rest for ever all doubts of my powers. The girls blushed up to the ears and turned away their heads, then looked again, and at length exclaimed, 'Oh, for shame!' and seeing me shaking it at them, Lucy gave me a box on the ear, saying, 'Put it away, put it away, naughty boy!'

Now a box on the ear from a young lady is, as everybody knows, a challenge, so I flung my arms round her neck and covered her with kisses.

Louisa laughed, Lucy struggled, but at length kissed me in return, and her friend came in for her share. We sat down on a bank and then commenced a good deal of badinage, fun and frigging, but as to the 'great go', I found that was 'no go', at all events, for the present. So after finishing our walk we retraced our steps to the pier, and so returned to Portsea Terrace.

On the way Lucy told me how it was she and her sisters were going out to India, for I had expressed some surprise that young ladies who possessed in so eminent a degree the *bel air* which the best London society can alone give to an English girl, should have been induced to expose themselves to all the vicissitudes of a tropical climate, when their charms would unquestionably be fully appreciated at home.

'I must tell you, my little friend,' said Lucy with an engaging smile, 'that our father, General W—r, was a man who cared for no creature but himself; returning to England after thirty years service in India, he married our dear mother for her beauty alone, she not having one shilling. He had amassed a fine fortune, and what do you think he did with it. He invested every rupee in the purchase of a government annuity for his life, taking no thought of what would become of us when he died. By this selfish act he secured to himself, with his general's pay, about seven thousand a year, and lived in great style in his house in Clarges Street. He gave us all expensive educations, and had us introduced into the best society, where we acquired the most expensive habits, and as great a taste for luxury as if we were each to wed a peer or a millionaire.

'The crash came at last, our father died – and what is worse, died in debt. Then it was that our dear uncle, the major, our mother's brother, came to our aid. The general had always treated him with great disdain, as indeed he did all our mother's relatives; but the good major was not deterred by that from offering us a helping hand.

' "My dear nieces," said he, "you will get from Lord Clive's fund just £50 a year a-piece, and that constitutes your entire fortune. Brought up as you have been it will not find you in gloves and shoes. So now, if you like to go out as governesses, I'll find you situations. If you prefer matrimony (excuse my bluntness), I'll take you back to India with me, pay your passage and outfits, and procure suitable husbands for you."

'There might be some brusqueness in the manner of making the offer, but we all three felt that it was kindly meant, so we accepted the "husbands" in prospect, and here we are,' and she rapped at the door of our lodgings.

While I was dressing for dinner, I could not but reflect upon the selfishness of old men in general, and the general in particular. Without the aid of the hearty old major, what a tissue of humiliations and distresses would have been in store for these three charming girls, nurtured in all the refinements and elegancies of life!

Now it happened that Mrs S—, the major's wife, had discreetly hinted to me that after dinner her lord was wont to take a nap, or sit and chat with her and his daughter, and that the young ladies would be very grateful to me if I would rise when they did from table and join them in the drawing-room. I bowed my acknowledgement and promised to take the hint, so after partaking but moderately of the dessert and contenting myself with two glasses of port, I rose up at the signal from our hostess, and accompanied the girls out of the dining-room.

There was always a lamp in the front passage, but the back one was rather dark, I therefore could not resist the opportunity of thrusting my hand down the bubbies of the delicious Lucy, who not seeing what I was going to do, screamed out.

'Hullo!' shouted the old major, 'what are you up to there? what's the matter?'

'Oh, uncle, how frightened I was! just as I stepped into the passage a horrid little mouse ran up my leg.'

'Ho! Ho! Ho!' roared the old boy. 'Hah! ha! ha!' then followed a tremendous fit of coughing during which explosion we all hurried pell-mell up the stairs to the drawing-room, Lucy paying me off with a terrible pinch on a part that shall be nameless, but I felt the nip all the evening.

What suppressed romping, what tickling, what fun we used to have in that queer, shabby, genteel lodging-house drawing-room every evening, while the jolly old major got bossey on brandy pawnee, or snored in his armchair till tea-time, and good Mrs S— and her plain daughter sat by darning stockings. Happy days, would I could live them over again!

Punctually at ten up came brisk little Mary with the tea kettle, and then brought in the formidable tea equipage. Then followed a rubber or a game at loo, and then to bed.

Now I felt in a little dilemma. I had two charmers to please, and both would be expecting me at the same time. Nothing offends a pretty woman so much as to find herself slighted for a rival. Besides, Mrs Fraser might be jealous, and as for Mary, she was so already.

While I was thinking about it, as I undressed for the night, who should pop in but Mary herself. I caught her in my arms; but the indignant little Venus gave me a great thump on the chest.

'Get out, you little brute,' she exclaimed in a rage, 'I've heard of your doings, I have. Yes, I heard Miss Lucy and Miss N—l talking about it all. As to your comforting that poor dear gentle Mrs Fraser, I didn't mind it; that is, not so much; but to take up with them bold young ladies who knows everything, it's too

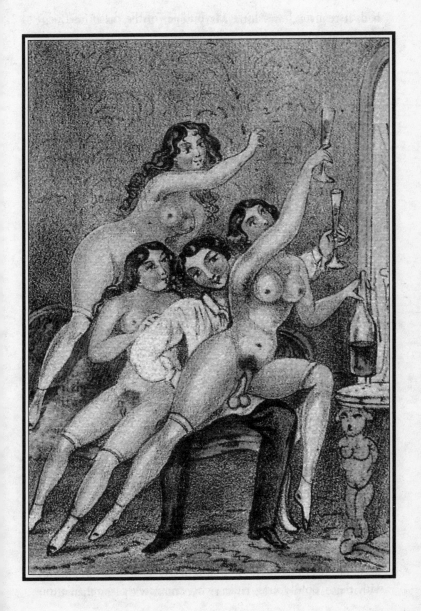

bad, it really is,' and little Mary began to cry as if her heart would break.

'For God's sake, my dear angel, don't talk so loud, Mrs Fraser will hear you; pray be quiet,' and I kissed her tear-bedewed cheek.

'Yes, it's all very well,' said the girl, 'you think I've no feelin', I suppose.'

'But, my pretty little cove, think of those fifteen or sixteen men you have had; consider, and be reasonable, I am only the seventeenth!'

'Ah!' cried Mary, 'you are only a baby that's clear, and know nothing of women; those fellows were all great hairy beasts of men, much older than me, and only had me because they paid in hard gold for my favours, but with you it is quite different – you are nearly my own age, you are young and pretty, and I love you – look in your purse and see what you have paid me, you'll find I never took the sovereign you told me to take, and more, I put back the five shillings you gave me.'

'Foolish girl,' said I, 'what's the use of getting spooney on a fellow who, you know, will sail when the wind changes, who could never marry you, and who in all moral probability you will never see again?'

'I know, I know,' sobbed poor Mary, 'but I can't help loving you, I suppose, you have a way with you that would captivate any girl, and if you are like this now, what won't you be when you are a man? But I'll forgive you this once if you'll only promise me one thing.'

'I'll promise you anything you please, my darling.'

'Well, then, swear to me you will never marry Lucy W—r.'

'I marry Lucy!' said I, laughing, 'why my dear little girl you must be dreaming. She is going out to India expressly to get a husband who has money, while I, I'm only a poor little cadet, with his pay and perhaps a hundred a year private fortune. What use should I be to her? No man with less than three thousand a year will suit her book; be quite easy, she will never marry me.'

'You swear it?'

'Yes, by Jove!'

'Then I will tell you something: she sleeps with Miss N—l every night, and they frig each other!'

'No!'

'It is a fact, I've seen them, and what's more they lick each other too.'

Now 'licking' in schoolboy phraseology, meant thrashing, so I stared in amazement at Mary, and said, 'Nay, if they thrash each other 'tis plain they are not good friends.'

Then Mary whispered in my ear, and opened a vein of knowledge of which I was before ignorant. The dear creatures were 'tribades'!

'The devil, and the devil!' said I, 'the nasty beasts.' Such was then my view of that most voluptuous Sapphic love, which now I fully understand and appreciate. 'Be easy, little Mary, I'll have nothing more to do with them, now give me a kiss.' She clung to me, I lifted her on to the bed and a rapturous embrace ensued.

When it was over, 'Now you are going to sleep with Mrs Fraser, are you not?' said she.

'That is so,' I said.

'Darling, I give you joy and I pardon you,' said little Mary.

'You're a jolly girl,' said I, 'let me give you a five-pound note.'

'Not for all the world!' said poor Mary, 'it would spoil all.'

'Why?'

'Oh. I don't know, but I don't feel for you the same as with other men; and, besides, I have eighty pounds in the savings bank.'

'You have!'

'Yes I have been well paid by the men I have had.'

'*Vous avez raison, ma chère.*'

'Oh, don't talk to me in that gibberish.'

'Well, I was only saying that you had reason to be well paid for you run great risks with those ship captains, who as a class are low brutes, and often diseased.'

'My God!' said Mary.

'Yes and some of these days you will be let in for a roarer.'

'A what?'

'A pox, my angel.'

'What's that?'

'A direful disease, which will destroy all your charms.'

'My God!'

'Truth.'

'Then you advise – '

'You to live a quiet life and marry some respectable young tradesman who can keep you in comfort before it is too late.'

'I walk out with such a one every Sunday now.'

'Then marry him, Mary, and believe me you will bless me every day you live for this advice – if you take it.'

'I will.'

'Really?'

'Really, I will, and I will write out to India to you, and tell you when I am married, and you shall be godfather to my first child. Now tell me how I am to address you?'

'You know my name well, "Cornet S—, Madras Cavalry, East Indies." I don't know what regiment till I arrive there.'

'One favour,' cried poor Mary, 'will you put on your uniform one night, and let me see you in it before you go, then I think I shall be happier, and whenever I let my husband have me, I will shut my eyes and think of you.'

'My darling Mary, I feel highly honoured, I'm sure.'

'Oh, Edward,' cried the poor little girl, 'Don't talk to me that way, I'm not a fine lady like your Miss Lucy's and your Miss N—l's, but a poor simple girl of humble parentage. Would you had been humble too, and then – then – but no matter, you will let me see you in your uniform once; only once?'

'Dear girl,' said I, 'no time like the present time, the wind may change tomorrow, and I may have to bid you adieu,' and I took out my keys and opened a portmanteau. I drew forth a superb uniform: sky-blue jacket, the breast one blaze of silver embroidery, with the same costly embroidery up each sleeve to the bend of the arm; cartouche belt and sword belt, all of silver lace striped with crimson silk; a pair of sky-blue trousers with a broad lace of silver down the sides; a pair of boots, with silver box spurs – Hoby's masterpiece (price three guineas); a steel scabbarded sword, straight and pointed; and the glorious shakoe or dress hat, with its plume of feathers – all of which I proceeded to don.

Poor little Mary was in raptures as she helped me to dress. 'Mars arrayed by Venus,' said I, conceitedly, but Mary had never heard of either Mars or Venus before, so the conceit and the flattery were lost upon her. The costume completed, I pulled on a pair of white kid gloves, then drawing my sword, I performed the salute as I would to my general, and dropping the point to the ground raised my left hand flatwise to my forehead.

'Oh how beautiful you are now!' cried little Mary, throwing herself upon my embroidered breast.

'Fine feathers make fine birds, Mary,' said I, 'but I would rather you'd admire me naked.'

'Then be naked, my own love,' cried the charmer.

By Jove, I pulled off that toggery a precious deal quicker than I had put it on, and stood stark naked before her. She caught me up in her arms with the strength of a lioness, and carried me like a baby to the bed; her tongue roved over my entire body like a lambent fire; she licked, she kissed every part of me, then tearing off her clothes with a frenzy almost allied to madness, she flung her lovely body upon me, joined herself to me, and gave me no rest for two mortal hours. At length she ceased, and rising up put on her clothes again; it was twelve o'clock.

'Mary,' said I. 'I have other work to do, you know it. I must have some refreshment; go, my dear love, and get me the wing of a chicken, a slice or two of tongue and a bottle of wine. I am quite famished.'

She hastened away and soon returned with what I required; I made a hasty supper and bade her good-night. She kissed me and wished me joy of Mrs Fraser. In point of fact. I lost no time in finding my way to the arms of that dear woman

'Truant!' she said, 'you are come at last then, I had almost given you up. I have been asleep, I think; dear me, what time is it?'

'Oh, about twelve, I believe, my dear, but never mind the hour.'

I passed a delightful night.

In a few days the wind changed, we all went on board, and the *Reliance* commenced her voyage down channel – but I am not going to inflict upon the reader the tedious narrative of a tedious voyage; I will content myself with relating a few curious anecdotes of some amorous adventures that occurred on the passage.

Lucy, her sister Fanny and the younger Miss N—l had often expressed their regret to me that we could never meet, except in the cuddy or on deck, where a hundred eyes observed our every gesture. I took the hint, and used to lower myself down by a rope into the quarter-gallery, and so got through the WC into their cabin, where we used to amuse ourselves by eating oranges, reading novels out loud, and by an occasional frigging (when Henrietta and the elder Miss N—l, who were the pink of propriety, were out of the way).

One day we three were diverting ourselves in this way, the weather being very sultry and the ship becalmed, when Lucy, who wore nothing but her chemise and a most fascinating *robe de chambre* of white linen, after letting me toy with and view her

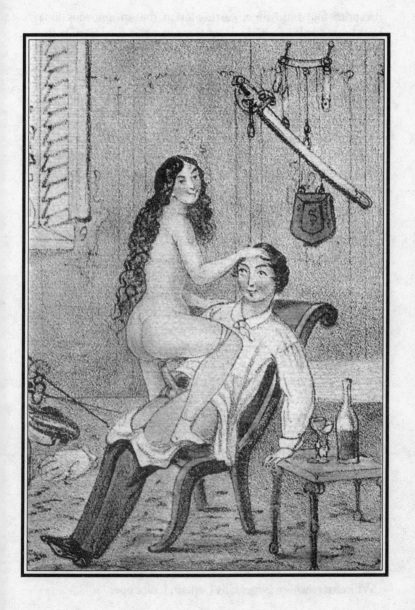

beauties for some time, casting upon me an amorous look, murmured half inaudibly, 'And is marriage so very terrible that girls always so much fear the first night?'

'My dearest girl,' said I, enchanted, 'there is nothing terrible in marriage, though it is true the maiden feels some pain at first. Will you let me show you what it is like? Do! do! I will be very gentle and stop the moment you tell me!'

She made some resistance at first, but as I was seconded by her friend, who represented to her that no ill could come of it as I was too young to do much mischief, she at length,

> Murmuring I will ne'er consent,
> Consented . . .

She had long been spending and I slipped into her in a moment. She gave one little suppressed cry as her hymen snapped, and then hugging me in her arms, threw her legs over my back, and abandoned herself to the joys of the hour. As for Louise, she could not restrain herself, so seizing me from behind, she began to rub herself against me with fury. When Lucy was satisfied, and I had a little recovered, her friend caught me in her arms, and worked me with such ardour, that ten minutes finished the second maidenhead. We were all in a bath of perspiration and quite exhausted. So I was glad to recline on Lucy's bed, while the fair creatures petted and fed me with oranges. What more we should have done I know not, but just as I was again getting ready for action, Henrietta came in. I seized on *The Fortunes of Nigel*, and commenced reading.

'Oh, here you are again, you young scapegrace,' said she, 'I wonder what Aunt S— would say if she knew that you came into our cabin every day to eat oranges and read Sir Walter Scott.'

'What, indeed!' thought I, but I did not say so. 'This is such an interesting tale,' I said, 'we had just got to the scene in Whitefriars where Nigel kills Captain Culpepper.'

'Really!' exclaimed Henrietta, maliciously, 'I thought it must be very exciting, for you all look quite flushed with the recital.'

This was so palpable a hint that I took an early opportunity to beat a retreat.

A few days afterwards I was proceeding to enter the quarter-gallery as usual, and watched for the roll of the ship to swing myself into it, when lo! I found myself in the lap of the virtuous Henrietta, who was performing a very natural office of nature there, and did not the least expect an intruder from the seaboard. So imagining me to be some dreadful kind of merman, she began to sing out like a stuck pig.

In a moment, and before I could extricate myself from the extremely delicate position in which I found myself, appeared Mrs S—, her lean demure daughter, the Misses N—l, Lucy and Fanny, and, oh! confusion worse confounded, the charming stewardess, Mrs Fraser. I was so completely overwhelmed by such an array, that without thinking what I was doing, I sprang at once out of the quarter-gallery into the sea. Being a good swimmer, and the ship being becalmed at the time, the only injury I sustained was a good ducking and the chance of being devoured by a shark, who made for me with great rapidity, but I dived under the ship's bottom, and coming to the surface on the starboard side, seized a rope which the seamen threw to me upon the cry of 'Man overboard', and was hauled on deck before the monster of the deep could catch me.

As soon as I had changed my clothes, I received a polite message from the captain that he would like to say a few words to me in his cabin. So thither I went.

The captain (who after all was in the right), gave me a tremendous wigging, 'You must know, sir, that I consider all the young ladies on board this ship under my especial protection, and I cannot allow any gentleman, however young he may be, to enter their cabins, least of all in the clandestine manner you have attempted to do.'

' 'Pon my life, captain, I'm very sorry,' said I, 'if I have infringed any of your rules, I beg to offer my apologies, I'm sure.'

'All right, my boy,' cried old A——ll, softened at once, 'you are a nice little lad, but remember that if your peccadillo should be worked up into a scandalous story, it might seriously compromise those young ladies' reputations, and what is worse, spoil their market.'

'Quite so,' said I, 'I fully see the force of your reasoning. It shall not occur again.'

'That's a good boy,' said the hearty old skipper, shaking me by the hand with a vigour that numbed the digits for half an hour and brought the tears to my eyes with pain, 'you'll do; you're not a bad sort, I see; pity your friends didn't make a sailor, instead of a soldier, of you!'

And so the matter ended.

A few days afterwards, the calm still continuing, the captain ordered the planks to be slung over the ship's side, and half a dozen men were set to scrape the sides, remove the seaweed and brighten up the copper a bit. Now this is a job that Jack has a mortal aversion to, and with reason, for while his head is exposed to the vertical rays of a tropical sun, his feet are ever and anon immersed in the briny element at the risk of being snapped hold of by the sharks! So poor Jack was not in the best of humour. Now it happened that an old weatherbeaten tar, while scrubbing the ship's side immediately below the quartergallery that had been the scene of my escapade, was suddenly startled by a most unseemly explosion above him which sounded amazingly like a rousing fart. As a natural consequence Jack cast his eyes aloft, and beheld a pair of enchanting white buttocks and a hairy cunny, such as had not blessed his sight since

The last time he parted at Wapping Old Stairs
With Sally . . .

But just as he was admiring these symmetrical proportions, there came unfortunately another explosion, immediately followed by a round shot which hit poor Jack in the eye.

'Damn my bloody eyes!' cried the tar apostrophising, I presume, the offended organ of vision, and being armed with a boat-hook to steady himself withal, he inverted it, and gave a thrust with the butt end, with so sure an aim that he effectually stopped the vent of the gun that had shot him. There was a screech, of course, and the insulted fair was rescued from her perilous situation, Dr Porteus being called in to examine the wound.

A report having been made to the captain, the following amusing dialogue ensued.

Captain on the poop, leaning over the starboard side: 'Hullo, you fellow down there.'

'Aye-aye, sir.'

'What are you up to you rascal?'

Jack: 'Scrubbing the ship your honour.'

Captain: 'But what have you been up to with that boat-hook?'

Jack: 'Holding on, your honour.'

Captain: 'Holding on, you damned tailoring son of a b—h! What have you been doing to the girl?'

Jack: 'Blasted b—h sh—t in my eye, your honour.'

Captain: 'No reason, you son of a sea cook, that you should b—r her with the boat-hook.'

As this elegant conversation was carried on in a loud tone of voice, it was of course heard by everyone on board, and considered a capital joke by all but the sufferer, who I lament to say was poor Mrs Fraser, who, alas! had already had quite enough of the 'butt end of the boat hook' before she came aboard.

I must confess, however, that it so disgusted me that I could never poke her again. The idea of so sweet a creature etc., etc., quite cooled my amorous inclinations. I was voluptuous but not dirty, and that shot which hit poor Jack in the eye had quite denuded me of my ardent passion for Mrs Fraser's charms.

She, however, got plenty of poking from the mates of the ship, from the officers who were passengers on board and, I believe (but 'tell it not in Gath, repeat it not in the streets of Ascalon'), from the captain.

Three weeks after we arrived at Madras, all the Misses W—r were married; start not, courteous reader, and do not condemn such a statement as improbable; I assure you on the honour of a gentleman it is the truth. Henrietta married Captain F— of the —th Light Cavalry; Lucy espoused Captain O— of the same regiment, brother of the Earl of O—w, of Clan—n Park, in the county of G—, while Fanny the little filly of fourteen, was led to the hymeneal alter by the eccentric Lieutenant E—, whose greatest ambition was to 'fuck a lady'.

And so I lost sight of the darlings and proceeded to join my regiment.

'Oh, it's all damned fine,' I hear some fellow exclaim, 'but you don't expect us to believe all this,'

' 'Pon my soul,' says I in reply, ' 'tis true as the – ' 'Gospel', I was going to add, but feeling how very little guarantee of truth there is in the comparison, I will say, as true as women have cunts – a fact the most captious will not dispute.

❧ 2 ❧

In which I demonstrate beyond dispute I am a man of mettle, by my amours with the native women

I had not been two days at the cadets' quarters at Fort St George, when I was ordered to do duty *pro tempore* with the —th Regiment at Vepery, a suburb of Madras, and I joined accordingly. There being a suite of rooms to let in the mess house, I preferred taking them to going into cantonments; they were only 50 rupees a month (£2 10s. 6d.).

Now it happened that the bungalow adjoining the mess house was an establishment for young ladies – i.e., 'half caste' young ladies. Now these, 'nut-brown maidens' (as Thompson, the poet, I think it is, calls them) were accustomed to bathe naked in a lake (*tank* is the Indian word), before sunrise, which *tank* had been constructed in their compound (*anglicé*, garden) for that purpose, and it also happened that my *dubash* (i.e. butler), who, *par parenthesis*, had a keen eye for his master's intrigues, had advised me of the fact.

The walls of the school compound were high, but as my rooms were upstairs and not on the ground floor of the mess house, I could very easily overlook them.

In India the houses are constructed with a deep verandah or

collonnade all round, so that the apartments may be shaded from the fervent heat of the climate; from the front of these verandahs hang mats or blinds made of the sweet-smelling cuscus root, and these are kept wet, by having water continually thrown upon them, so that the air, however hot it is outside, enters the verandah and house at once cool and fragrant. It is very easy to see through these blinds from within, but persons outside can discern nothing. Every morning then, the moment I got out of bed, I would seat myself in a lounge chair, and with a cheroot and a cup of coffee, sit and smoke, watching the gambols of the young girls in the water.

The sight I then obtained so fired my imagination that I conceived an ardent longing to be amongst them. These half-caste girls have generally remarkably fine figures – some of the girls before me were perfect. Their hair was particularly luxuriant and beautiful, and one or two had pretty faces, though it must be confessed a slight tint of the rose would have freshened them up wonderfully. However, Europeans get used to pale cheeks in time.

I called to Ballaram, my *dubash*; he was a fine looking fellow of the Mahratta caste, who never did any work, but merely catered for my table, and kept the other servants in order – a sort of gentlemanlike major-domo in fact. He approached as grave as a judge.

'You are a man of experience,' said I, 'cast your eyes over those girls and tell me which will make the best bedfellow?'

Ballaram examined them attentively.

'For make fuckee business, sahib, that girl who is splashing the other one would be too much good, but if master thinks about preety facee and fine body, the missee who is squeezing the water out her hair very brabher hie.'

'Do you think any gentleman has had her yet?'

'Dat ting who can tell, sahib?'

'But I suppose the old women who keep these schools turn a

47

pagoda or two now and then by means of these girls who after all are only the daughters of small shopkeepers in the Black Town; of what manner of consequence can be the reputation of the little daughter of a half-caste shopkeeper?'

'All that too much true, sar. S'pose the Colonel Sahib, or the Major Sahib, or any other burra sahib [great man], happen to cast his eye that way,' and he inclined his head towards the school, 'and him say, "Boy, go, bring me such a girl," ah, that bhote brabher hie [very proper]. Him boy say, "Bhote eucha, sahib" [very good, sir], and him run to old lady mistress and say, "The burra sahib wantee such a girl, put a veil over her and let her come."

'Then old lady mistress askee, "You money got?" "Yees!" him answer, "How much rupee?" "Very good, backsheesh, ma'am, fifty rupah." "Fifty rupees not 'nuff, must have eighty rupees, you tellee Colonel Sahib dat girl one virgin."

'Den burra sahib get angry, and he make send sepoy and angry chit [note], and he threaten old half-caste woman to send to jail for being procuress, and he frighten old she too much, so she send little missee, and she take the fifty rupees, and Colonel Sahib have girl all rightee. But s'pose little young Cornet Sahib, like your honour, do this, then master get too much trouble, get in what you call one great row, master savee.'

'Yes yes, I see what you mean, but what force won't accomplish, money may.'

'That one very good word, sahib, but master's pay only two hundred and ten rupees a month, that not too much money.'

'But I have money at my agents, Messrs Parry, Dare & Co. At all events I must and will have that girl.'

'How much you givee, sahib?'

'Well, eighty rupees [£8], if she's a virgin, and fifty rupees [£5], if she's been poked before.'

'Bhote eucha, Sahib, master dress and go banker's and bring back pica [the money], and then I make all brabher.'

'And when shall I have her?'

'Today night.'

I continued to watch the girls till they had done bathing, and then having breakfasted, I was off to my agents in a *palankeen* as fast as the bearers could trot. I brought back the money in gold pagodas (a beautiful coin about the size of an English half-crown, and worth seventeen rupees, or thirty-four English shillings).

'There' I said, as I shot them out on to the table in one golden glittering heap, if that sight does not make the old girl's mouth water I don't know what will. But, harkee, Master Ballaram, take care I'm not made a fool of, for if the affair fails, I shall dismiss you from my service.'

'Har – why sar? you don't want to talk that way, master gentleman, no; I only too much poor man, I master slave; what him say it same as if my God say it – de girl sall come.'

'Yes,' said I laughing, 'but in the meantime I'll put the pagodas under lock and key – tell the old woman you have seen the money, that it is all ready, and upon her bringing the girl here tonight at ten o'clock, it is hers.'

Ballaram looked vexed, but promised compliance.

'If it is all right I have a pagoda for you.'

'Bhote eucha, sahib!' and he made his *salaam*.

I sat drinking my wine at mess till half-past nine, and then retired to my apartments, and lighting a cheroot, waited with the greatest expectation for the happy moment. At about three minutes to ten Ballaram appeared, and in a mysterious whisper told me the old woman and the girl were below.

'Quick!' said I, 'show them up.'

The next minute two muffled figures appeared, covered from head to foot with a thick native veil of crimson muslin edged with gold. The stoutest of the two I conjectured was the old harridan herself, so I said, 'Good evening, madam, be seated, pray,' and I placed two chairs on which they sat down.

'Good evening, sare,' replied the old woman, 'I have brought missee, you see, as you wished, and if you really have the money your *dubash* mentioned, I leave her with you till half-past four tomorrow morning, when I will call for her, before anybody is about. But I must have my rupees at once.'

'With all my heart,' said I, unlocking my cash box, then resting my arm upon it I added, 'be so obliging as to remove your veil and that of the young lady, that I may see that she is the same I expected.'

'But the money sare, the money!'

'Is here,' said I.

'Well, sight for sight,' said the old crone, 'dat fair; show me your money, I show you the gal.' I turned the key and threw up the lid, the old woman cast her muffler off her head and sprang forward. At the sight of the gold pagodas her eyes sparkled, and she tried to clutch them.

'Soho – gently – gently! you have shown so much distrust of me that you must pardon me if I doubt you; there is the money, you see it, I will count it if you please; prove to me that you have brought the right girl, and it is yours.'

I thought the old devil looked a little confused, but she unmuffled the girl in an instant; to my surprise she had nothing on but the crimson wimple, so there she stood naked and grinning before me.

'It won't do, old lady, won't do at all, this is not the young lady, as you know quite well.'

In fact it was the 'splashing' girl.

'She is fine piece,' said the old woman deprecatingly, 'she'll know how to please you; as to the other she's no good and too much shy.'

'Oh! damn it all,' said I, 'what an old humbug you are; I tell you, I'll have the other one or none, so come – troop – shog off;. come back with the other, or not, just as you please; if you do, here's the money, if you don't, not a rupee – begone.'

As she went out, I heard her say to Ballaram, in Hindustani.

'What a sharp little fellow he is, that master of yours.'

Ballaram twirled up his moustache, cast upon her a glance of supreme disdain, but vouchsafed not a word. So the old hag began to hobble down the stairs, followed by the equally discontented damsel, whom I did not admire in the least, and who gave me an angry glance, which I replied to with 'a snipe'.

As soon as they were gone, I called Ballaram. 'You see,' said I.

'What I do, sar? how could I help it. Dam old woman understand too much well, but she try to put off her old stuff on you first. S'pose master like other young gentleman, griffin you call dem, you pay money first, and find out not right gal after. Old woman not know you not like other griffin, sahib.'

'But I want the girl, and I suppose she won't bring her now?'

'Not bring – never fear. She back 'gen presently.'

He was right, in about ten minutes she returned, and pushed the girl into the room with an angry gesture. 'There she is sir, take her and give me the money,' and she roughly pulled off the girl's muffler, and spite of her modest struggles to retain at least some part of it, presented the beautiful creature naked to me. She was the same girl I had seen wringing the water out of her hair in the school compound. I handed over the pagodas, which the old crone carefully counted; then, tying them up in a red cotton handkerchief, she hurried away. I sprang to the door, bolted it and then caught the dear girl in my arms.

She was quite young, but her breasts were fully developed, firm and pointed; only a slight quantity of hair had begun to sprout on her mons Veneris; her waist was small and round, and her hips singularly large and bulging, with the most splendid buttocks imaginable; her hands and feet were exquisitely small, and there was a pensive expression in her childlike face, which was very winning.

'Come, my pet,' said I, caressingly, drawing her on to my knee, 'let me give you a glass of wine; try these mangoes, they are very fine.'

'I feel so ashamed,' she said, trying to hide her face.

'Nonsense!' said I, 'never mind me, I'm only a boy, you know; now if it had been the old grey-headed colonel, I shouldn't be surprised; come, give me a kiss.'

This she did, and so electrified me, that I could not restrain myself, and began to kiss and pull her about, to all of which she made great resistance.

'Then you really never yet have had a man?' said I.

'No, never I assure you.'

'But you know all about it, I suppose, my dear?'

'Oh – yes – many of the girls have been with the officers four or five times, and they tell us about it; so, of course, we learn everything.'

'Well, my darling, drink a glass or two of wine, and have some mangoes, we will chat a little while.' She did so, and seemed to enjoy the fruit and wine. 'Now dip your pretty little paws in this basin of water, here's the towel, that's the ticket. Now let us make love.'

Presently I asked, 'What's the name of the old woman, my girl?'

'Mrs Aventura.'

'Do you like her?'

'Who, I, sir? I can't endure her.'

'No?'

'She's a dreadful old woman.'

'Is she though?'

'Horrid.'

'Why?'

'Oh she will make the girls do the most shocking things with quite old men – if they only pay her well.'

'Pooh, my dear, that is very natural, the old girl only wants to make up a purse, I suppose.'

'Yes, but most of the girls don't like it, especially the little ones.'

By this time I was frigging her with great assiduity.

'And you, my dear, how do you feel, do you think you shall like it?'

She cast down her eyes pressed her cheeks against mine, and whispered, 'With you I think I shall, but not with old men.'

I gently laid her down on the bed, and taking off my shirt and *pajamahs* (loose silk drawers), I lay down beside her and told her how I had seen her bathing, how much I admired her and how I was determined to have her. Then I mounted her and began to drive at her virgin cunny. What a tight little box it was. I'm afraid I put her to considerable pain, for she struggled and cried very much; but, what was curious, whenever I offered to release her, she only hugged me the closer, and tried to smile through her tears. This conduct on her part so captivated me that, thrusting with double vigour, at the fourth push I went through all obstacles up to the hilt. She groaned and sobbed, exclaiming, 'Oh, oh, how dreadfully you have hurt me. Oh, I shall die!' But presently a soft languor pervaded her frame, she kissed me gently and began to spend. What a delicious moment it was. After a time, my climax almost coming, I clung to her with fury, grasping and feeling every charm, and then sent a rushing torrent up the rosy passage.

For some minutes afterwards we lay without sense or motion, prostrate on the bed, but coming to by degrees, we began to toy and kiss, and soon wrought ourselves up to the same state of excitement we had before been in, only this time her shyness had a good deal worn off, and she seemed as willing for the play as myself. In fine, I passed a most delicious night, and so got into the good graces of my companion that she promised so soon as I joined my regiment at Cannanore, which I was to do in a fortnight (being only temporarily attached to the one I was then with), to endeavour to escape from the school and join me there.

But matters turned out very unfortunate for the furtherance of our little game. I suppose I may have indiscreetly talked to some of the officers of the regiment about the fine girl I had had, and at length it came to the ears of the colonel. He set his spies to work, and soon wormed out the whole story. Then I was sent for, and severely reprimanded for 'the great impropriety of my conduct'. I was 'reported' to the Adjutant-General, and was ordered to join my regiment forthwith. Having thus, rather unscrupulously, got rid of me, the old scoundrel sent for Mrs Aventura and asked her how she dared to let one of his subalterns take precedence over him and have the pick of the girls?

The old lady, plucking up some courage, replied with asperity that for her part those who paid best were the customers she most liked. That the young gentleman had very handsomely given her eighty rupees, while he, the colonel, never yet gave her more than fifty, and she added that she thought she had been bullied by him long enough. The colonel was furious, he swore that unless she immediately brought him the girl, for whom he would not pay her a single piçe, he would send in such a report of her conduct as would lead to her being indicted 'for corrupting the morals and extorting money from young officers', when she might rely upon it her school would be broken up, and herself sent to jail.

Terrified at these threats, she drew in her horns, and promised compliance, so poor Lillias was carried off to the old rascal, spite all her tears and opposition. But she was a resolute girl and, indignant at the way her young lover had been treated, enraged at the compulsion employed upon herself, she defied the colonel to his face, called him a mean wretch, and upon his offering to salute her with a kiss she spat upon him. The colonel coolly wiped his face with his handkerchief, called his servants, and having made them tie her down upon the cot in his room, ravished her on the spot, in spite of her cries and struggles. Having done this, he unbound her, for she had fainted, turned her over, and tied her again in a different position, and having put a bolster under her belly to raise her posteriors well up, the cruel man administered a severe castigation with a rattan; then making her put on her clothes, he kicked her into the street. Poor Lillias managed to crawl as far as Mr A——, the District Magistrate, and told her story; a surgeon was sent for, who examined her, and the whole matter was reported to government.

Meantime Mrs Aventura, having heard how her pupil had been abused, decamped in the night with all her money and jewels, and was never more heard of. As for the colonel he was brought to a court-martial, and having first been dismissed the service, was then transported for seven years by the civil judge for the rape and assault. Lillias went back to her friends.

I read the whole affair in the newspapers at the time, and soon forgot the adventure, in the gaieties of Cannanore. My reputation had preceded me, and on my arrival I found myself caressed by all the ladies, and my society sought after by the men. I had a happy knack of telling a droll story and could set a whole mess table in a roar at something I had said, without allowing any smile to appear on my own lips. It is a great secret in telling a funny anecdote, or giving vent to a witticism, for so sure as the narrator or wit smiles at his own joke, his listeners will compose their countenances into gravity, and if he adds, as some really witty fellows do, 'Not bad that, eh?' then woe to him, he will at once be voted a bore, and never more listened to.

I now commenced a regular course of fucking with native women. The usual charge for the general run of them is two rupees. For five, you may have the handsomest Mohammedan girls, and any of the high-caste women who follow the trade of courtesan. The 'fivers' are a very different set of people from their frail sisterhood in European countries; they do not drink, they are scrupulously cleanly in their persons, they are sumptuously dressed, they wear the most costly jewels in profusion, they are well educated, and sing sweetly, accompanying their voices on the *viola da gamba* a sort of guitar, they generally decorate their hair with clusters of clematis or the sweet-scented bilwa flowers entwined with pearls or diamonds. They understand in perfection all the arts and wiles of love, are capable of gratifying any tastes, and in face and figure they are unsurpassed by any women in the world.

They have one custom that seems singular to a European – they not only shave the mons Veneris, but take a clean sweep underneath it, so that until you glance at their hard, full and enchanting breasts, handsome beyond compare, you fancy you have got hold of some unfledged girl. The Rajpootanee girls pluck out the hairs as they appear with a pair of tweezers, as the ancient Greek women did, and this I think a very preferable process to the shaving.

It is impossible to describe the enjoyment I experienced in the arms of these sirens. I have had English, French, German and Polish women of all grades of society since, but never, never did they bear a comparison with those salacious, succulent houris of the Far East.

But although immersed in this voluptuous debauchery, I did not entirely neglect my fair countrywomen. I found time to go to balls, routs and dinner parties; I found time even for hunting and shooting, and studying the language and dialects of the country.

What an exciting, jovial life it was!

Amongst the ladies of the cantonment was one who more particularly took my fancy: she was the wife of a Major T—, of HM's —th Dragoons, a lovely blue-eyed blonde of twenty-two, blooming and fresh as a daisy. Her husband was sixty if he was a day, and most incontestably to prove himself an ass, had married her from a Hammersmith boarding school, some five years before, that is, when she was seventeen. She had then seen nothing of the world, and hardly knew what love was. But the major was her guardian, and thus secured to himself both her person and fortune, which was considerable. To this sweet creature I paid such marked attention that we soon understood one another. She the more readily accepted the intrigue as my extremely youthful appearance, to a certain extent, disarmed scandal, and she wished to draw off from the public eye her real *cavaliere servente*, Captain M—, by whom she had had a child, which passed for the major's. Indeed, Major T— was very fond of the little fellow, and devoutly believed he was of his own begetting. But all this I found out afterwards.

The major was a great invalid, and had a separate room, but seldom essaying to perform his marital duties, and signally failing when he did try. This was the state of things when I set my wits to work how I might seduce this beautiful, but artful woman. I used to pass hours at her house nearly every day, hold the silk she wished to wind, turn the leaves of her music book while she played or sang at the piano, and make sketches in her album, and everything that lovers could say to each other we had said. I had had my hand down her breasts and up her clothes many times, and she would sit with me on a sofa in the darkened room (all the apartments being kept very dark in India to keep them cool), with her hand in my trousers, manipulating for half an hour at a time.

Occasionally the poor major would look in, seem pleased to find me there, instead of Captain M— (whose presence always made him uneasy, I could not tell why, as he was not of a jealous nature), and would accost me with, 'Ah, young S— there you are again, making love to my wife, you young dog!' and he would laugh good-naturedly, and slap me on the back, and wily Mrs T— would say, 'Oh yes, he's a good little boy, and as long as he is so he shall be my knight and wear my colours.' Poor old major, if he had only known, but he did not know, and hadn't the shadow of a suspicion of me! *Tant mieux*.

Now it happened that one day I had dropped in as usual, when Mrs T— told me, with an arch look, that the major was gone down to the Presidency on an affair of business and would not be back for a week, and that, it being the native festival of Huli, she had allowed all her servants to go and see the show, except the gardener, whom she would now tell to deny her to any visitors who might call. She went on to the verandah and gave him orders and returned to me. I threw myself into her arms.

'Not yet, not yet! my dear boy,' said she. 'I must first go over the bungalow and see if those rascals have fastened the doors and jalousies, for in their absence some scoundrel might enter the premises and rob the house, and – and – ' she burst into a laugh.

'We might be surprised,' said I, completing the sentence.

'Good,' said she, 'that is just what I mean.'

We secured the jalousies and doors, and carefully searched all the rooms. Satisfied that all was safe, I went with her into her chamber, when, having double-locked the door, 'Now, my dear love,' said she, 'do what you like, I am all your own!' In a minute we were both naked, sporting on the bed. Then for the first time I had a full expansive view of that lovely woman. I revelled in the woman's cunt with its luxurious fringe of fair locks that curled above, on the sides, and beneath it. I never saw so much hair on a woman before; she had quite a forest under her arms. It was a novelty to me, and pleased me; I entwined my fingers in it, I combed and parted it, and overcome by an irresistible lust, ended by gamahuching her, to her great delight. I had so wriggled about, that at length I got astride of her with my rear pressed down on her glorious great bubbies, and felt them rise and fall as they panted with desire. Presently she grasped my thighs, and raising me up, took my pestle in her mouth, and sucked it with such ardour that I feared every minute she would either bite it off or swallow it whole. Suddenly she stopped, exclaiming, 'Oh, 'tis too much! I cannot bear it another instant; turn round! put it in! fuck! fuck! do fuck me!' I lost no time in complying. Then she clasped me with such strength, she murmured forth such lascivious words, she did such lascivious things, she quite frightened me. Why this woman, said I to

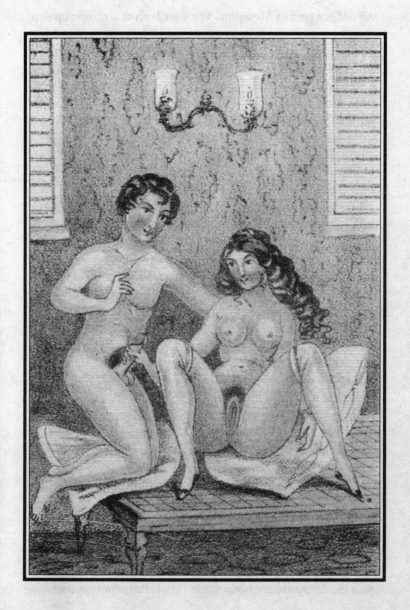

myself, is a perfect Messalina. We were both so wrought up that in ten minutes our climax came; gods! how she ground her teeth, how she bit, pinched, and thrust her finger up my — . And then we both lay panting, quite exhausted.

At length, recovering a little, she wiped her beautiful face with her handkerchief, saying faintly, give me the eau-de-Cologne off the dressing-table, and open a bottle of claret; you will find some in the cooler in the corner of the room.

She deluged her fair body with the eau-de-Colgne and then playfully threw a quantity over me. We soon finished the delicious cool wine, and so to bed again.

I begged her to kneel up that I might have a full view of her hinder beauties. She complied at once. Oh, what an enchanting prospect was before me. Imagine a skin white as alabaster, a slender waist, a Spanish back with a delicious fall in it, over which meandered her waving golden hair, imagine hips of enormous size terminating in a bottom the largest, the most dimpled and the whitest I had ever beheld, supported on thighs so rounded, so symmetrically proportioned, so altogether ravishingly exquisite that an angel of light could not have withstood such temptation. I stooped down and buried my face in those hills of snow, then rising up, I slipped with ease into her mossy grotto, and at it we went again. She jutted her bum out to meet my thrusts; she stretched straight out first one leg then the other; she passed her hand between her legs and felt my wand as it went in and out; she toyed with the balls of Cupid, and soon brought down another sweet shower.

'Oh, you're a man! a man!' she said, 'more charming by far than M—; he shall have me no more, sweet boy-faced fellow, I am thine for ever,' and she sank fainting on the bed.

When she had a little recovered, I asked, 'What have you done with little Jack?' (her son).

'Oh,' said she, 'Mrs B— so often asks me to let the little man pass the day with her children that I could not refuse, you know.'

'Ah I see; bright idea, wasn't it, today?'

'Very.'

'Hark! what's that,' and she sat wildly up in the bed.

'Somebody trying the door of the entrance-hall, and violently too,' said I, coolly.

'Up, quick, my love! do not wait to dress, gather up your clothes and get out of the window; run down to the border of the *tank*, hide yourself in the *tope* [grove], dress there and take the boat; flee! quick, begone.' I grasped my clothes; to unfasten the jalousie door, to spring out (fortunately we were in a one-storeyed house), to run like a madman across the lawn at the back of the house, to gain the *tope*, was the work of an instant, but even as I fled I heard a tremendous crash – the front doors had been burst open. But I knew her door was double-locked. I knew before the intruder could make that yield, she would have time to put the bed in order, to close the jalousies, to cast on her *robe de chambre*, to put out of sight the claret bottle and the glasses, and I was content. I dressed myself, and unmooring a little sailing skiff which the major kept for his diversion on the lake, I leapt in and, hoisting the sail, was soon a hundred yards from the shore. Then, indeed, I turned my head, and saw a man running at full speed down the jetty – by the time he reached it I had gained another fifty yards; he raised the gun which he carried to his shoulder and whiz, crack came a shot, slap through the sail and about a foot above my head. Well aimed, old fellow, said I jeeringly to myself, before you load again I shall be out of reach. But load again he did, and that rapidly; crack went another shot, but it only splashed harmlessly in the water, fifty paces astern of me. Well, to be sure, said I, you're a paladin, my fine fellow, whoever you are, but you're not the major, that's certain, he could never have run like that.

Concluding that my enemy would mount a horse, and gallop along the bank after me, I made for the shore at once and starting off through a belt of jungle, the track of which I knew quite well, from having often had a day's sport there, I reached my bungalow half dead with the heat, for it was barely three o'clock, the hottest part of the afternoon.

I drank some brandy and soda-water, and after I was cooled a little I took a tepid bath. Nobody was at home but my *choera*, a pretty little boy about twelve years of age. This boy, Muniah his name, was very fond of me, and once when I was ill, nursed me with the greatest tenderness. 'Boy,' I called; in the Madras Presidency all servants answer to the name of 'Boy', even if old grey-headed men. I addressed my haughty, high-caste *dubash* as 'boy' occasionally, just to keep him in his right place, though sometimes I called him by name, in compliment to his superior attainments and his caste. In Bengal, servants are called by, 'Qui hie?' (Who waits?)

'Boy,' said I. Muniah appeared.

'Muniah,' said I (a great compliment, he not being of high caste); he made me a low, a gratified *salaam*. 'Do you know where I went this morning?'

'Ho, sahib [yes sir], sahib ke jana Bhebee Sahib T— [my gentleman went to Mrs T—].'

'How do you know that?'

'I heard master tell the bearers to take palankeen there.'

'Bhote eucha [very good],' said I. 'Now mind, pay great attention to what I am going to say. If any sahib asks you where I went this morning, you must say that I have not been out, that I am not well, do you understand?' (All this in Hindustani.)

'Quite understand, sir.'

'That's all right, now brandy pawné lao [bring some brandy and water], Argh lao [bring a light], and a cheroot.'

I lay down on my cot and smoked. Presently I heard the galloping of a horse at speed, the horse was snorting as if distressed, the rider pulled up with a jerk at the door.

'Sahib hie [is you master at home]?' roared the voice of Captain M—.

'Yes, sir.'

'When did he come in?'

'Master has not been out this morning,' said the boy, innocently.

'Not been out? You lie, you *soure* [pig].'

'No sir, I tell truth, sahib not well; sahib not been out at all since yesterday.'

'Very odd,' said M—, in English, 'can I see him?'

'Hullo! is that you M—?' said I, from within, 'come in, old fellow, glad to see you.'

He entered, he looked heated and troubled, and was covered with dust and his horse's foam. He beheld me in an immaculate clean cambric shirt, and striped silk *pajamahs*, languidly lolling on my cot, smoking, my face pale and unheated. He was evidently staggered.

'And you really have not been out this morning, S—.'

'Out, by Jove! what should I go out for in this broiling sun, and I as seedy as be damned. Oh, those blasted fellows of the —th Dragoons, they sewed me up damnably with their bad wine. In "our service", you know, old fellow, we always give our guests good wine.' (The king's officers were always sneering at the company's, and used to say in "our service" we do so and so, but then we are royal regiments, who serve a crowned head, and not a lot of beastly merchants.)

M— winced, and bit his lip. I surveyed him with the utmost nonchalance, from head to foot; he was a powerful man, and could have made mincemeat of me in a moment.

'But, my dear fellow,' said I, affecting a fashionable drawl, 'what the devil's the matter with you, you look so deucedly excited, is anything up?'

'Up! Yes, by God, something is up!' cried M—, dashing his fist down on the table, 'and curse me if I don't fathom it.'

'Ah, weally!' said I, with the most imperturbable coolness as I blew out a cloud of smoke, 'try a cheroot, old fellar!' and I handed him my case.

M— took the case and lit a cheroot; while pulling at it he suddenly raised his eyes; they met mine. What he read there I don't know, but he gazed at me long and fixedly, without saying a word. 'Now is the time of trial,' thought I, and I continued steadily to meet his threatening fierce eye, with an expression half curious, half languid, my brows slightly raised, and a cynic smile (I felt it must be cynic) on my lips, from which ever and anon issued volumes of smoke.

'Damn it,' cried M—, 'either you are really seedy, and have not been out of your bungalow, as you say, or you are the most perfect specimen of duplicity and coolness I ever met.'

'You flatter me,' said I, with a faint smile.

'Flatter you! by Jove! Look here, old fellar, if you have been out of the house, you have been to Mrs T—'s, and if I thought you had been there, I'd kill you,' he roared fiercely .

'Now, my dear M—, pray talk any rhapsody you please, but have a little mercy on my nerves!' said I, coolly, but to say truth I was in a most damnable funk.

'Then you really have not been out today?' said he, cooling down a little.

'Captain M—,' said I, rising, and making him a bow, 'when I tell a gentleman one thing, I don't mean another. If you think I'm a liar, say so like a man, and I shall know how to avenge myself for the insult!' and I bent upon him a look so fierce and defiant, that the strong man cast down his eyes; in the boy of seventeen he had found his match.

'But, sir,' I went on, 'as you have done me the honour to mention the name of that most virtuous lady, whose husband's friend I am, may I be permitted to enquire, Suppose I had been there this morning, what business is it of yours? You are not her husband, or the friend of her husband – nay he detests you – and I tell you, as a friend, that it is currently reported you are the father of her child. Now, mind you, I pry into no man's secrets, it's nothing to me one way or the other, but if you, undermining the affections of that lady for her husband, have seduced her, very ill it becomes you to fall foul of any lovers, other than yourself, that she may have. You have seemed to imply that I am one; look upon me, look upon yourself,' and I pointed to a mirror, 'would a woman who would choose a stalwart like you, condescend to a mere boy like me?'

He seemed convinced, and took leave, saying, 'Forgive me, S—; I am sorry I offended you, but you don't know how much I love that woman.'

'My dear M—, she has deceived her old, confiding husband and, believe me, she will deceive you; there are no bounds to women; when once they fall – they fall, there's no chaining them up, it's the common lot! Good-morning. Oh! by George, how precious hot it is,' and I ran in from the verandah.

He galloped off in the sun. 'Now that fellow will run his thick head against a stone wall, and get the poor woman into trouble, by Jove, he will,' thought I.

❧ 3 ❧

In which are given some little episodes commonly called 'lovers quarrels'

When I woke up the next morning, the first thing I missed was my watch. It was a gold Barwise, and had belonged to my father; it was worth forty guineas.

'Damn it,' said I, 'I would not lose it for a trifle and the chain was worth twenty.' I never dreamt of suspecting my servants, they were true as steel. I must have left it at Mrs T—'s. By and by a peon came with a written advertisement (in those days when a man wanted to advertise, he wrote his advertisement, engaged a messenger, and sent him round to every resident in the cantonment). I took the paper and read as follows:

> Whereas some gentleman, unknown, left a valuable gold watch and chain, maker's inscription, 'Barwise, No. 1,739', at a lady's house, last evening, this is to give notice, that the owner may have the same on applying to Captain M— of HM's —rd Foot. If not claimed within ten days, it will be sold to defray expenses.

I handed it back to Muniah; he hesitated and looked at me. 'Cuah munchta [what do you want]?' said I.

'The sahib's watch is here described,' said he.

'Pooh,' said I, 'take the paper away.' He did so. By and by a

66

bearer brought a dainty little three-cornered note. I opened it and read:

DEAREST BOY – I hope you got off all safe. M— was furious, for 'twas he, my friend; he burst open my door also, and behaved like a great brute as he is. I was lying down on the bed, all had been put straight. He swore terribly, and told me I had been untrue to him, that the gardener had told him little S— was with me, and little S— he would find and cut his throat!

I laughed at him, told him he had no right to intrude upon me, that if I had received him as a lover, he was not my husband, and had no right to be jealous of me; that as for me, I would have as many men as I liked, but that I preferred men and not babies like little S—, that little S— had not been there, and the gardener did not know him, and had mistaken somebody else for him; that I would not deny that a gentleman had been there, and one whom I liked much better than him! and that he might go to the devil for aught I cared.

'Oh!' said he, 'I may go to the devil, Clara, may I?'

'Yes! you great bullying beast, as soon as you like! What right have you to interfere with me, and break into my bungalow? I am only sorry my servants are not here that they might throw you into the *tank*!'

'Very well, madam,' said he, restraining his rage, 'I'll go since 'tis your wish, and I'll take this handsome gold watch and chain with me!'

Then, dear S—, I saw that you had left your watch, and I'm so sorry. Tell me its value, and I'll send you a cheque, you know I've lots of money.

He took one of my husband's rifles and ran down to the jetty. I saw you got off safe, God bless my dear boy! But now! send me a line, and say you are not going to fight. Ah! he will kill you, my own! he is a dead shot. Write at once to her who loves you more than life.

Your devoted,

CLARA

'Boy,' I cried.

'Sahib!' said Ballaram, advancing.

'The buggy, quick!' (The buggy is a hooded gig, something like a cabriolet.)

'Yes, sir.'

The buggy came to the door. I leapt in and drove rapidly to Captain R——'s quarters; he was a noted duellist, and a capital second; better still, he was a man of honour. I told him the entire story.

'Your advice, R——,' said I, 'what is it?'

'Keep quiet, old fellar, and sacrifice the watch.'

'Can't be done,' said I, 'it was my father's, I would not lose it for a cool hundred.'

'Deuced awkward,' said R——. 'I'd buy it myself at the sale but you must see that whoever undertook to buy it for you would be supposed the owner, and have to stand up at twelve paces before that devil of a shot, M——.'

'I quite see that; but, suppose I go and claim it myself?'

'Of what possible good is even a gold Barwise to a dead man,' said R——.

'Stop a minute, my dear friend,' said I, 'don't arrive at hasty conclusions. Tell me, you are a man of experience; according to the present code of honour, has the challenged man the choice of weapons?'

'Undoubtedly; but everybody fights with pistols nowadays.'

'Pardon me, *I* don't.'

'No?'

'No! I fight with the rapier.'

'You? why you are a boy, what do you know of the foil?'

'Everything! *carte*, *tierce*, *volte* and *demi-volte*. I am a pupil of Angelo!'

'You are!'

'Yes, by Jove! and I mean to have my watch!'

'All right,' said R——, coolly, 'come along, we'll go and claim it, but mind, whatever he says, whatever he does, let him give the challenge. He shan't hurt you; he is a big fellow, I know, but I'll protect you; is this your buggy?'

'Yes.'

We jumped in and drove straight to Captain M—'s. A whole lot of fellows were there smoking. I knew most of them.

'Devilish lucky for you they are here,' whispered R—, aside.

'How are you, M—,' said I.

'How are you?' said he, shortly.

'You have found a watch, I believe?' I asked.

'Yes,' said he.

'Will you let me look at it?'

'Certainly.'

'Ah! thank you, that is mine,' and I flung the chain over my neck, and put the watch in my pocket.

M— gave me a look of concentrated fury. 'Do you know, S—,' said he, 'if these gentlemen were not here I would strangle you!'

'Really!'

'I would, by God!'

'Then you would have been hung for murder.'

'I don't care!'

'Come, come!' said R—, 'this won't do old fellar, if you have any grievance against young S— you've got your remedy, but I won't allow him to be insulted.'

'You be damned!' cried M—.

'All right, old fellar,' said R—, 'we'll settle our little affair afterwards, but, meantime, what have you got to accuse little S— of?'

'He's a blackguard and a scoundrel,' roared M—.

'You are a scoundrel yourself, M—,' said I, 'and have seduced Mrs T—. You are a coward and a beast, who has bullied her and me, you great blundering brute.'

'Very well, my little fellow, you shall pay for this bravado.'

'All right,' said I, 'my friend R— will receive any message you

69

may wish to send,' and hooking on to R—, he and I strode out of the bungalow and drove off.

'You did that capitally; now you're all right; he never had a rapier in his hand in his life. He is a horrid bully, and I hope you pink him.'

'I'll try my best to do so.'

'Good! Now it's nearly seven, I'll come and dine with you.'

'With great pleasure,' said I, and we drove to the mess house and played a game at billiards, while waiting for dinner. At dinner I called twice for champagne, and made R— as welcome as I could. My brother officers looked curiously at us; nobody ever asked R— to dinner unless a duel was on the *tapis*.

Dinner was over and we were sitting on the verandah smoking when J— of the —th approached.

'I want a word with you, R—,' said he.

R— rose up; they walked in the compound together. R— came back looking very merry.

'Well?' said I.

'All right, old fellar; with swords, tomorrow at six, at the old pagoda near the *tank*; but have you any weapons?'

'I have a pair of the finest rapiers you ever saw; they were made by Rivière, of Paris, and my great grandfather bought them there in 1742.'

'Did he fight?' asked R—, with much interest.

'Oh, yes, he killed Lord R— with one of those swords in the Bois de Boulogne the next year.'

'Really!'

'Yes.'

'You come of a good lot then?' said R—.

'Pretty well; but wait.'

Punctually at six we were on the ground next morning. R— held the swords in their antique shagreen case under his arm. We had not been two minutes on the ground when M— and J— appeared.

M— looked very pale, but he sought to throw off his evident trepidation by an apparent bravado. 'It seems,' said he, laughing with great contempt, 'that if I escape the spit of young S—, I am to try my Joe Manton's with you R—.' (Manton was the great maker of hair-trigger duelling pistols in those days.)

'With all my heart,' said R—, 'you're a good shot, and I'm not a bad one, I hope I may get the chance, old fellar.'

'Gentlemen! gentlemen!' said J—, 'this is not *en règle* at all. I cannot allow this. You have the swords, R—, permit me to inspect them?'

He opened the case, measured them carefully, weighed them in his hand, and then said, 'It seems to me this is the best weapon, don't you think so, M—?'

'I know nothing about rapiers,' said M—, with disdain, 'I thought they were exploded with the last century, give me whichever my opponent rejects.'

'Not so,' said R—, 'my friend desires you will take your choice.'

M— chose the sword his friend had pronounced the best and we set to work.

Poor M— knew nothing of fencing, that soon became manifest; I was young, I had a heart then, I did not want to kill him, so watching a chance I ran him through the sword arm. The blood spurted out, the seconds interfered, but M— swore a great oath and said if I did not kill him, he'd kill me. His arm was bound up with a handkerchief, and he attacked me with the wildest fury; but I had not learnt of Angelo for nothing, and parried all his lunges; but at length he ran in and made such a desperate pass at my breast that I was obliged to *volte*, so that I received him on my weapon, and he fell back dead as a stone. They raised him up, but he never spoke, and so mounting our horses we rode off.

'It's just as well as it is,' said R—, 'for if you hadn't killed him, I should.'

Of course there was a court of inquiry and all that, but it being proved that I was the challenged party, I was released from arrest and ordered to return to my duty, Brigadier L— merely observing to me that it was as well to abstain from such *rencontres* in future, as they were quite contrary to the Articles of War.

Now it is very absurd, you will say, but I must confess I felt that poor fellow's death poignantly; after all he had been wronged, though not legally, and the respect which it procured me, did not compensate for the anguish I endured at having cut off in the prime of life a gallant young fellow of twenty-eight. I felt this for years afterwards. I often feel it now, and would give all I possess to be free from the stain of that man's blood.

Yet such is life, and so inconsistent is human nature, that it did not prevent me from passing the next night in the arms of Mrs T—, who called me her little Cid, her true knight, and caressed me in the most flattering manner. I told her I was sorry I had killed him; she laughed and said, 'Why, you silly boy, did he not take two shots at you, and the first that went through the sail seems to have gone very near your pretty little head. If he had hit you it would have been murder; your affair is a mere matter of course, an affair of honour, be easy.'

'But he could not fence, he knew nothing of the straight sword,' said I, 'it would have been more plucky if I had let him use his own weapon.'

'Nonsense, silly boy, he would have shot you through the heart as he did T— and D—, and poor young K—.'

'Has he killed so many?' said I.

'Oh, yes, he was a Goliath of Gath with the pistol, but my little David has slain the giant!'

I was a little comforted at this information, and began to think that it was just as well that M— was out of the world, but I would rather that R— had killed him than I .

However, I threw off the megrims for the nonce, and gave myself up to the enjoyment of Mrs T—'s perfections.

What a happy night we had! what gamahuching, what fucking, and what a delicious supper she gave me. With her for the time, I was a little hero, and Venus never served Mars with greater *empressement* than that lovely girl did me that night.

Women may sometimes like a smooth cheek, and a boyish figure, but they adore a brave heart, and she thought me a worthy gallant. But, in point of fact, I had little to boast of but a skill in fencing.

'Tis true he had little to boast of but a correct eye at twelve paces, and would have killed me to a certainty; still his not being a hero did not constitute me one, and spite of all the flattery I received from her and others, the adulation of young ladies and the gracious looks of the men, many of them veterans in war, I was not happy at the result of that ever to be lamented duel.

Now although Mrs T— was certainly as fine a woman as any man could desire to possess, she was so very lustful and insatiable, that a very few days of her company sufficed to cloy me and cool my ardour, and the last night I passed with her I had some difficulty in bringing a second embrace to a satisfactory conclusion, notwithstanding all the blandishments of that lovely woman, so true it is that too much of the same pleasure wearies and nauseates in the long run. I was, therefore, not sorry to remember that the major would return on the morrow, and cut short our amorous meetings.

But there was, perhaps, another reason for my waning passion. I had made the acquaintance of a delicious creature, the wife of an artillery officer, to whom I paid great attention.

Mrs B— was just eighteen, and had been married about six months, she was the *beau idéal* of a pretty English girl. She had fine blue eyes, full of expression and even fire, an oval face, luxuriant chestnut hair and a charming figure. I admired her extremely, and did not attempt to conceal my admiration.

She evidently understood my glances, for she returned them, but steadfastly repelled all attempts at caresses. One fact I had ascertained to my great satisfaction, she did not care two straws for her husband; he, foolish man, had not succeeded in pleasing his young wife. She had married him to comply with the wishes of her friends (like most girls who go out to India), because they assured her he was a suitable match, and could offer a handsome settlement, and found out too late that he had nothing in his temperament to suit her ardent nature.

Now it happened at this time that the officers were getting up some theatrical performances, which were to precede a masked fancy dress ball, and the only obstacle they met with was to find officers sufficiently young, clever and willing to undertake the female parts.

A deputation from the theatrical committee waited upon me and exhausted all their persuasions to induce me to take the part of Laura in *Love, Law, and Physic*, but I absolutely refused. 'I'd no idea,' I said, 'of being turned into a girl just on the eve of a fancy ball.'

By and by some of these fellows went to dine with Captain and Mrs B—, and complained very much of my obstinacy.

'Perhaps,' said Mrs B—, 'a lady might be able to induce him to comply; accept my good offices.'

They were delighted, and tendered her their thanks.

The next day she invited me to *tiff* (lunch) with her, *tête-à-tête*. I accepted the invitation with rapture. As soon as we had got all we wanted, she told the servants they need not wait, and at once opened the campaign. I began to relent.

'But, my dear Mrs B—,' said I, 'I shouldn't know how to dress myself, I've no idea in the world how women's clothes are put on. I should make of myself the greatest guy in the world.'

'But suppose,' she said, with a bewitching smile, 'that some lady were to offer to be your tirewoman; suppose, for example, I were to consent to dress you?'

'You!'

'Yes. I myself!'

74

'In that case I would undertake to act in twenty farces!' cried I after reflecting for a moment. 'But your husband, what would he say to that?'

'My husband, indeed! I hope you don't suppose I ever allow him to intrude into my dressing-room! You are very like a young lady who arrived at the cantonment the other day, a Miss J—. I happen to know she is not well, and as she has often been here, if the servants see you, they would merely say if asked that Miss J— had been with me; that is after I have dressed you, mind, prior to that you must not be seen by any mortal, and must come through the plantation at the back of the house, to my bathroom window, which opens on it; you will find nobody in the garden. Sit down under the window till I come to you.'

'At what time?' cried I, enchanted at the prospect of an intrigue so completely after my own heart.

'Oh! about half-past seven or eight; I shall take an hour to metamorphose you; but remember one thing, you must not smoke one cheroot all day tomorrow, or you will spoil a little afterplot on which I have set my heart.'

While she was talking, I had stealthily passed my right hand under the fall of the tablecloth, and was toying with her polished thigh about two inches above her garter.

'Don't be rude,' she whispered. 'Imprudent boy, don't!'

I gave her a look.

'What wicked eyes you have!' she whispered again.

'Everybody else says the same thing,' said I, 'but this plot of yours – tell me your plot?'

'You know Feridoon, as they call him, Cornet F—, of the —th Cavalry,' said she, blushing prodigiously, and pushing away my hand, which I had forced higher up her thigh.

'Oh, yes, the ass!'

'Is he not!' said she. 'Well, before I married, he had the effrontery to pay his addresses to me! and, since my marriage, has so persecuted me with his attentions, that everybody has noticed it and my husband has spoken to me about it. I told him I detested the fellow and that he was welcome to kick him out of the compound, or set his servants to do it when next Mr F— had the presumption to call. This pacified Charlie, and he took his measures so well that I have not seen my persecutor since, but I want to be revenged on him, and as my revenge is a mere harmless joke, you must assist me.'

'With all my heart,' said I, 'only tell me what to do, and I'm your man.'

'Well,' said the dear creature, smiling archly, 'after the play is over you must put on a mask and get into my *palankeen*, apparently to go to your quarters to change your clothes, but instead of taking you there, the bearers shall have orders to make a detour and deposit you at the ballroom door. I shall be sitting on the first couch on the left-hand side; you will come and seat yourself beside me. I shall introduce you to F— as Miss J—, he will ask you to dance, and you will keep him at work all night, and torment him a little, won't you dear!' and she put her hand down to squeeze my leg; but I had released a certain prisoner who had long been rampant, so that when she put her hand down she caught hold of — !

'Oh, you naughty, naughty boy!' she exclaimed, snatching away her little hand, but at the same time blushing and smiling. 'You'll torment him, won't you?'

'You shall see,' said I.

'Well then, *au revoir*, little S—, till we meet tomorrow evening!'

I cast upon her a look full of love and took leave.

Punctually at half-past seven I took up my post under the bathroom window of pretty little Mrs B—.

After waiting about a quarter of an hour the jalousie was opened! how my heart beat with expectation!

'Are you there S—?' said a soft whisper.

'Yes, my angel.'

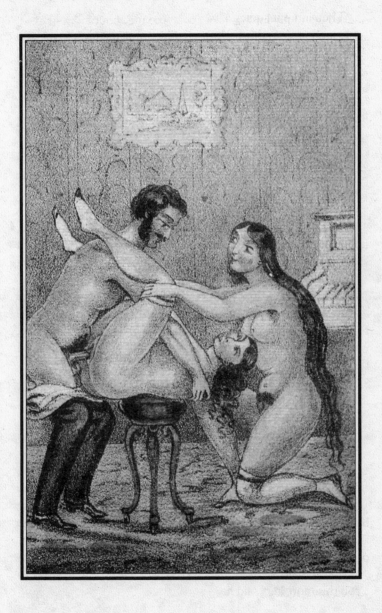

'Then jump in, quick!'

I sprang into the bathroom. She immediately closed and bolted the jalousie blinds. I threw my arms round her waist and covered her face and neck with kisses.

'Do be quiet, you naughty tiresome boy! leave off, sir! you'll make me angry presently.'

'Nonsense, Ellen!' I whispered passionately, 'we understand each other!'

'And if we do,' said she gravely, 'that's no reason you should compromise me. My husband is at home, dressing for the ball, so you must restrain yourself. Now, mind not one word even in a whisper,' and she led me into her dressing-room, where a lamp was burning. She then bolted the door opening into the bathroom, and signed to me to strip. Never did I denude myself of my clothes so rapidly. She let me draw my shirt over my head, but when I was going to pull off my trousers, 'Stop, stop!' she whispered, scarcely above her breath, 'you need not take those off, you can roll them up above your knee.'

'I'll be hanged if I do,' said I in the same low tone of voice, and before she could prevent me they were off, and stark naked I stood before her, stiff and erect!

'Oh, you naughty boy, this is too bad! it is indeed!'

'Ellen, I must have you! indeed, indeed, I must!'

'Oh, my God, no!' she sighed out still in a whisper.

'Then I'll go away,' said I, 'I can't stand this,' and I began to pick up my clothes.

'Stay!' she said, laying her hand on my arm. There was a magic in that monosyllable. I caught her in my arms and bore her blushing to the bed. I had just got into her, and was in the height of bliss indescribable, when there was a knock at the door, 'Well! what is it?' said she sharply.

'Ellen, my love,' said her husband, 'have I left my razor strop in your dressing-room? I fancy I did, when I came in to speak to you this morning,' said he.

'My dearest love, I don't know, I'm sure, but I'll look. I'd open the door and let you come and look for it yourself, but Miss J— is with me, and we are both undressed. I'm going to take her to the *bal masqué*, you know; dear me, no I can't see it anywhere, how very tiresome, you can't have left it here, dear!' said the little puss.

'Oh, never mind, my love,' said poor B—, 'don't trouble yourself, I beg!' and away he went.

'Oh, how he did frighten me!' said the poor little thing.

'Never mind, dear, it's all right now!' and I plied her with vigour; my hands roved over every beauty; soon her eyes swam in tears of delight, she flung her limbs around me, she kissed and hugged me, and soon our climax came.

'Oh, oh!' she whispered, 'I – am so – afraid I shall sc–ream, delicious!' and we lay melting in bliss.

But soon recovering ourselves we renewed the soft encounter, and when that was over, we rose up to dress. She put the bed straight, tied my clothes all up in a bundle, and dropped them out of the bathroom window into the garden; then putting rapidly upon me one of her laced chemises and handing me a pair of silk stockings, and rose-coloured garters, she clapped on my head the most perfect female wig I had ever seen; it had springs which made it fit close to the head, and the parting was white silk. I glanced at the mirror, and did not know myself in the least. I beheld a laughing rosy girl, with a profusion of dark brown hair falling in ringlets all over her shoulders; it was myself. Then I put on a pair of white satin shoes and she laced up my stays and put a great pad of wool for each breast and a padded belt on my hips; then came three petticoats, then a white muslin dress, made rather high in the neck, and with short sleeves; then she placed a real rose in my bosom, ruthlessly ran a great needle through both my ears and hung in a pair of superb emerald earrings, flung a necklace of pearl round my neck, which, with my face, she powdered, and then, handing me a pair of white kid gloves, she pronounced me perfect. I glanced at the mirror again. It was truly wonderful! Then she began to dress herself, I assisting her and kissing her lovely back and shoulders and breasts all the while. She had got on her chemise and was lacing her stays when there came another rap at the door; she ran and opened it. It was B—.

'Sorry to disturb you, my pet,' said he, 'but are you girls coming with me in the carriage, or do you take the *palankeens*?'

She opened the door wide enough to let him see me as I stood with my back to the door, and then said, carelessly, 'Why, no dear. I shan't be dressed for some time yet – you see I'm half-naked – so I won't keep you waiting, poor old boy; but keep places for us at the theatre, near you, you know! Ta, ta!' and she shut and locked the door again.

When we had heard the carriage drive off, I said, 'Why did you open the door and let him see me! what an imprudence.'

'Little simpleton, not at all! he only saw your back, and he saw that my companion was really a young lady.'

'Yes,' said I, 'and he saw that muslin dress, and will recognise it on the stage, and will know that I am not a young lady.'

'For which reason we will change it, my dear, put on this lilac silk, your figure is so slight it will fit you I'm sure.'

'If you're going to take this muslin dress off me, I know what I shall do before you put the other one on.'

'Now, now, naughty.'

'Yes, dear Ellen, do, do.'

'Well, be quick then,' and she unfastened the dress; it was off in a moment, and we were on the bed in a trice. What a rapturous fuck it was!

When we had a little recovered ourselves I said, 'But there is yet a difficulty to be overcome. It is clear if I act the part of Laura in this lilac silk, I must change it ere I take the part of Miss Jermyn in the ballroom; spite of my mask and your fair protection, I should be detected by the dress, which would spoil all.'

'For which reason,' said the clever little woman, 'you will be brought back here by my bearers, and you will tell my *ayah* [maid], that you don't feel very well, that you will lie down for half an hour, and then go to the ballroom; you will then lock that door and change your dress again, substituting the muslin and rose for the lilac silk and brooch. She will not see the lilac silk at all, as I shall lend you my white capote which will envelope you from head to foot; when you have got the lilac dress off, you will fold it up carefully and put it into that drawer, and lay the muslin one over a chair; at the expiration of half an hour, call my *ayah*, and let her help you on with the muslin dress, telling her that you took it off before lying down, fearing you might tumble it.'

'Why, I declare!' said I looking at her with admiration, 'you have a real genius for intrigue.'

'You flatter me.'

'I – not at all; you are a buttercup; kiss me darling!'

She did so.

'Well now we're ready, let's be off,' and away we went.

My *palankeen* deposited me at the stage door, her's took her to the dress circle.

'What have you done with your fair companion, my love?' said her husband as he made room for her beside him.

'Oh, isn't it tiresome,' said she, 'she does not feel well, and is obliged to lie down, poor dear; she won't be able to come to the play, but she has promised to join me afterwards at the ball.'

The curtain drew up, and the farce commenced. I was well up in my part, but having to appear at the window of a romantic-looking cottage, and respond to the enamoured strains of my gay Lothario, as the devil would have it, I made a sad mistake, for be it known that the reverse side of that romantic cottage was a mass of whitewashed boards and dirty cobwebs, and against this ricketty erection was placed an equally ricketty ladder, on which I, poor Laura, was standing, in imminent peril of my neck; when, therefore, Lothario, falling on his knees, exclaimed, 'Allow me to salute you *à la militaire*!' I was so flabbergastered that I quite forgot what pretty reply I ought to make; whereupon the prompter, Captain P—, gave me a tremendous pinch in the calf, exclaiming, 'Damn it, why don't you answer,' this in a whisper. But I, feeling the pinch, and forgetting my character, shouted out, 'Damn it, don't pinch so.'

To hear the lovely Laura use such an expression at such a sentimental moment, of course, set the house in a roar of laughter, while ironical bravos saluted my ear on every side; as for poor Lothario, he looked ridiculous enough still kneeling before the cottage.

Silence being at length restored, Captain P— went on the stage and thus addressed the audience: 'Ladies and gentlemen, Miss Laura begs to offer her humble apologies for the slip of the tongue of which she was guilty and promises not to offend in future, if you will allow the piece to proceed.'

The play then went on, and the curtain fell at length amidst loud applause. Laura was called before the curtain, was loudly cheered, made her bow and hooked it.

Strictly following the directions of Mrs B—, I lay down for half an hour then called the *ayah*, and by and by appeared in the ballroom in the muslin dress and masked like the rest. I seated myself near Mrs B—; her husband was standing by.

'How do you feel now dear?' said she.

'Thank you very much, I am better now, my headache is gone, and I feel pretty well.'

'I'm so glad, dear.'

'Shall you dance tonight, dear Mrs B—?' said I.

'No, my love, I think not! but here comes Mr F—, he's so fond of dancing.' F— advanced rather timidly and bowed.

'Why Mr F where have you been this last week? I have not seen you for an age,' said she, giving her husband a droll look.

' 'Gad I've called a good many times on you, my dear Mrs B—, but you were always denied to me.'

'Really, how sorry I am!'

'Perhaps you'll make a fellar amends by dancing with him?' said the lout.

'Couldn't do it my good man, I am quite tired, I merely intend to look on; but here is my friend – Miss J—, Cornet F—; Cornet F—, Miss J— She will be happy I'm sure.'

'Vewy prowd, miss, I'm sure,' said F—, with an awkward bow.

'Oh, I love dancing,' said I, with a languishing air.

We stood up; I danced eight sets with him and two waltzes, and never parted with him an instant. At four in the morning he took me in to supper, I devoured nearly a whole chicken, four slices of tongue, and drank nearly two bottles of champagne. F— regarded me with a sort of grotesque horror, and I heard him whisper to a friend,

'Such a devil of a girl! I'm nearly dead, by Jove; she eats and drinks like an ogress.'

I had the greatest difficulty in restraining my laughter. As for the ladies they regarded me with amazement.

Supper over, I rose up and whispered to F—, 'Take me into the ante-room, my garter has come down.'

F— offered his arm with a nervous air; arrived in the ante-room, I put my foot upon a chair, and pulling up my clothes about four inches above the knee, said, 'Well, put up my garter, you fool, can't you?'

F— plucked up his courage and performed the office required, but then took the liberty of slapping my thigh; I administered such a box on the ear as sent my gentleman flying to the other end of the room, where catching his spurs in the door mat, he fell to the ground. I walked off and seated myself beside Mrs B—, and told her the sequel.

'He'll find you out, my friend,' said she.

'Not a bit of it,' I said, laughing, 'if he talks of my dancing and eating, and the garter, you will say to everybody that he is a mean fellow, who took an unwarrantable liberty with the poor girl.'

'Very well, but now, my dear boy, you must go; remember you go straight into my dressing-room, strip as quick as possible, put all the things in the bottom drawer, then get out of the bathroom window and put on your own clothes, and get home as soon as you can. I'll detain Charlie here another half-hour, that will give you time; good-night.' I pressed her hand and left. I found my clothes under the window, and was soon fast asleep in my own bungalow.

It was eleven o'clock the next morning before I opened my eyes, I sprang off the cot, plunged my head in cold water, drank a cup of coffee, lit a cheroot, and seated myself in my easy chair on the verandah, as right as a trivet, but that was my 'age of iron'. In youth we can do such things, and all is *couleur de rose*, but grown old and grey, we succumb at last.

F— was furious. He saw that Mrs B— had played him a scurvy trick, but being a fool, he never fathomed it.

In relating this anecdote to my friends, I have been wont to embellish a little, and have told them that I declared myself to F—, and apprised him who Miss Jermyn was; such was not the case, it was never known to anyone but Mrs B— and myself; nor should I now tell the story, but, alas, dear Ellen, her husband and F— have been dead for years, and its narration can do them no harm, though many of my contemporaries yet living will recognise the initials, and remember the circumstances.

A few days afterwards the whole cantonment was scandalised by an affair that happened.

Mrs T— had supplied my place with young B— of the —th Dragoons and he used frequently to pass the night with her.

One night it happened that a servant, to whom she had spoken harshly, having previously had some suspicions of her fidelity to her lord, took it into his head to watch her through a hole he had made in her bedroom door. The patience of these natives is proverbial; he watched patiently till one in the morning, then he heard three raps at the jalousies of her bedroom (the window); she sprang out off the bed and opened them and young B— leapt in. They stripped themselves naked, she got on the top of him on the bed; the servant ran to his master's room and told him; the major, without making any noise, placed two men with loaded pistols under the window, with orders to shoot any person who came out, and then seizing a heavy horsewhip, went and burst open his wife's door; he surprised them in the act; he flogged his wife till the blood ran in streams; B— sprang out of the window, and was shot down by the watchers. The major, quite exhausted, went and locked himself in his room. They flung B— into the lake, but he managed to get out, and crawled home with his right arm broken, and a ball in his groin.

The next day the major was found dead in his cot; the excitement had killed him, he had broken a blood vessel; he died without having time to alter his will, and Mrs T— retained all his property and her own; she removed B— to her house and nursed him in his illness; he sold out of the service, and they returned to England together, but whether he married her, or what became of them I could never learn. This affair made a great noise at the time, and seemed to render other persons who were carrying on intrigues very circumspect in their behaviour.

As for Mrs B— and myself, we arranged a plan by which it was next to impossible for a discovery of the amour to be made.

She used to visit me at night, enveloped from head to foot in a native veil, and often when my servants thought I was entertaining some Mohammedan girl, I was in fact enjoying the society of my pretty Ellen.

A year thus slipped pleasantly away; we had become very spooney on each other, and this dangerous sentimentality would certainly, in the end, have led us into a scrape. But fortune was propitious enough to order it otherwise. Captain

B— received a staff appointment in a distant district, and we parted with eternal vows of constancy, fidelity and eternal love!

> Some natural tears we shed,
> But wiped them soon.

In fact, before she had been gone a week, I found consolation in the arms and charms of the enchanting Mrs H—. She was extremely beautiful, but had one defect – her teeth were bad, and when she opened her mouth she spoilt her face, yet I used to say of her that 'she was pretty in spite of her teeth'. And many others thought so too. Her husband was a 'prig', and an old woman to boot. He was a great poultry fancier, so while he disported himself with his cocks and hens, I made love to his wife. She had a brilliant complexion – a lovely white and red – her hair was black, her eyes hazel; she was of a nature to feel passion, and of an age to declare it – in fine, she was piquant. But all her charms were lost on her *sposo*; he was a little plain mean-looking fellow, with a squeaky voice, and looked like a eunuch! Heaven only knows if he was one; to add to his defects, he was a 'Newlight', as the would-be saints of those days were called. I never knew a more contemptible creature; he stood in some awe of his handsome wife, who took care to have her own way.

As I did not admire bad teeth, I would only poke this woman in one way, and that was *en levrette*. She made great opposition at first, but soon got to like it, especially as I said to her, 'My love, in this attitude you gain an inch.' She had the most splendid back, and her hips and nether hemispheres were superb; her breasts, however, were not perfect, and not so firm as I could wish. At the end of three months we tired of each other and parted; I returned to the native girls, while she threw herself into the arms of Lieutenant W— of the —th N. I.

After I had been ten years in India, I took my furlough and

returned to England. I had been very fortunate in the number of deaths that had occurred among the officers of my regiment, and found myself a captain at six-and-twenty, a rare thing in the company's service. I had quite resolved to lead a bachelor life. But my excellent mother, luck, Providence, or what you will – decreed otherwise. My mother had been plotting and making up a match for me before my arrival. The lady was a reputed heiress with an estate of twenty-five thousand pounds; an only child, her parents declared that they could not let her go out to India – so my resignation of the service was made a *sine qua non*; how I could have been so besotted as to comply with this absurd condition, I know not; but so it was that having ascertained that the estate really existed, and finding the young lady had considerable personal attractions and seemed inclined to like me, I yielded in an unhappy hour to the solicitations of my mother. We were married.

After the ceremony we started in a carriage and four for Dover *en route* for Paris, and at that gay capital we passed the winter of 1844; we spent about fifteen hundred pounds in the five months we were there, the money being supplied by her mother from time to time. All this was very well, yet strange to say I grew very discontented; my wife was exceedingly jealous, so that whenever I even looked at a pretty face, I was treated with a pout, or a fit of the sulks, or with tears, which made her eyes red, and spoiled their expression. I began to long for the freedom I formerly enjoyed; and I found, too late, that fetters may be irksome, even if made of gold.

My temper soured, I was *ennuié*, hipped and miserable. We returned to England; there a new annoyance awaited me; that dear mother-in-law of mine told me we had been very extravagant and must retrench; that she had taken and furnished for us a pretty cottage in Devonshire, and that in future her daughter's allowance would be four hundred a year. I was furious, and gave vent to my wrath in no measured terms; my wife took her mother's part. Upon this extra aggravation I told them that they might both go and live at their pretty cottage for aught I cared, or go together to the devil; but as for me, with all my friends in town, and me the darling of the ladies – go, I would not. There was, of course, a regular row; the two mammas-in-law quarrelled.

Then came recriminations; each old lady accused the other of plotting and match-making, and to make an end of a long story, my wife went home with her mother. I accepted one with mine, and returned with her to Bruton Street. I never spoke a word till I found myself *tête-a-tête* with my mother that evening after dinner.

'My dear son,' said she, 'I am sorry to see you so much concerned; those people have behaved shamefully!'

'Mother, you have married me with a vengeance!'

'My dear child,' cried the old lady, 'do pray consider I did it all for the best, the girl seemed such a sweet creature, and so young too, scarcely seventeen, and you know the estate exists; how unhappy I am!'

'My dear mother, you have simply ruined me, that's all! only ruined me. I had got my captaincy, my pay was pretty good, and with the hundred and fifty pounds a year Uncle Charles left me I did very well. I was not in debt. I enjoyed life. But now with respect to this precious estate of theirs . . . My solicitor has been down to D— Hall, and made some enquiries on the spot; subsequently he has made some enquiries in town; the estate turns out to be heavily mortgaged, the trees have been felled in the park, and the old man will soon be "up country", as we used to say in India. The estate is not entailed, and, in short, you have married me to a pauper in fact! with her eight quarterings, and an escutcheon of pretence in the centre. Bravo! clever mother!'

'My dear, dear son, you astonish, you shock me beyond expression! and is it so bad then, and will your wife have nothing?'

88

'Next to it,' said I, 'she has a hundred a year she inherited from her grandmother, and she may get another hundred out of the wreck of her father's property, that is, if he does not mortgage every acre before he dies, the brute!'

I did not see my wife for two years, during which I had a dear girl in keeping, at a little suburban villa, and occasionally diversified my amusements by an amour of a more *recherché* character, and was beginning to feel tolerably contented again, when one morning there came a very peremptory letter from my father-in-law.

After reproaching me with neglecting his daughter, he went on to say that he was somewhat embarrassed in his affairs, and could no longer afford to keep her, and added that unless I at once took her back, or made some suitable provision for her, he should put the matter in the hands of his solicitor. 'Pooh!' said I, and I tossed the letter into the fire with the greatest contempt. But there was another letter, I recognised the handwriting, it was from my wife. It was couched in terms so humble, so affectionate, so everything that the most exacting of men could require, that, deceived by it, I relented.

My mother wrote to her; she joined us in Bruton Street; I gave up my suburban villa and my fair friend, and tried to hope we might yet be happy. For the first month all went well, but unhappily, among my mother's servants was a little parlour maid, a sweet pretty creature, the daughter of a tradesman. She had received a pretty good education, and was not at all like a servant, either in manners or appearance. I had seduced this girl, though she was but fourteen, before my wife came up to town, and the difficulty was how to carry on the amour after her arrival without being discovered. Little Emma cried bitterly when she heard who was coming, and from the first I saw the two girls took a mortal dislike to each other, yet all went well for a month. At the end of which time, unfortunately my mother was obliged to go into the country to see a relative who was ill.

No sooner was she gone than my wife betrayed a jealousy and a vigilance of Emma that almost debarred me from ever even speaking to the dear little girl. So I had recourse to the pen, and wrote Emma a long letter, enclosing a five-pound note and assuring her that my wife, who was very religious (God save the mark!), would certainly go to church the following Sunday, and that then we should get a chance. This note, by the aid of honest John my mother's footman, and half a sov., I managed to get conveyed to her.

I woke up with a (pretended) severe headache, and declared I felt too ill to get up. My wife was all obsequiousness and attention, and herself brought up my breakfast (I knew quite well why). She even offered to stay at home and read the church service to me, and a sermon! But I affectionately declined, and begged she would not remain away from church on my account. So to church she went. When the bells had done ringing, I rang the bell. To my surprise John appeared.

'Hullo, John! where's Emma?'

'Now, Master Edward, you are too bad, indeed you be!'

'Damn it, man alive! where is she?' and I gave the poor old fellow, who had known me from a child, one of my fierce looks.

'Gone to church, sir.'

'Gone to church! by whose orders?'

'Mrs S—, sir.'

'The deuce!' and I looked so wretched, that honest John took compassion on me.

'Mrs S— watched her out of the house, sir; but Emma's a clever girl, she'll be back directly, now the bells have done.'

'My dear old John, you restore me to life,' and jumping out of bed, I hugged the old man in my arms.

Just then Emma entered, I ran to her and carried her to the bed. 'Go now, John,' said I, 'you're a real trump, you shall be well paid for this service,' and I pushed him out of the room, and locked the door. Then I tossed up the darling girl's clothes,

I gamahuched her, I fucked her on the spot. What a scene it was! we had both fasted so long that we were quite rampant. How she flung her fair limbs over my back! gods! how she spent on the bed; how she bit, wriggled and fucked. Oh! it was delicious. Again and again we returned to the charge! we took no heed of time. Just as we had died away in our third embrace, there came a rapping. 'For God's sake, sir!' said poor John in a subdued and agitated whisper, 'Mrs S— is coming up the stairs.'

Sauve qui peut! became the order of the day. Emma dashed into my dressing-room, and as madam opened the bedroom door, made her exit by the other and reached her own room in safety. I turned my face to the wall and pretended to be asleep. I heard the rustle of my wife's silk dress as she swept into the room, and trembled.

'And how are you now, dear?' said she, seating herself on the bed.

'Eh! ah! who's that? Ah! I believe I was asleep.'

'Poor fellow!'

'Oh, never mind,' said I, 'it is quite time I was awake.'

'How's your head, poor old boy?'

'Better, thank you, love. I shall get up, I think.'

'Do, darling, if you like.'

'Yes, I will,' said I, and I flung first one leg and then the other out of bed.

'Why, dear me, how flushed you are,' said she.

'Yes, I feel rather feverish.'

She felt my pulse, 'Why you are in a high fever; what a pulse!'

'Oh, damn the pulse, I shall be cooler after my tub,' and I made my exit into my dressing-room and locked the door. Refreshed with my cold bath, I dressed and descended to the dining-room. I was hungry, and luncheon looked tempting. The sherry I knew was good; a man stands on no ceremony with his wife, so I set to work. It never occurred to me till I had finished, that it was odd she didn't come down. But then it struck me all at once, and I began to reflect: 'She has been examining the bed, or she has found a shoe or a garter or something belonging to that poor little girl.'

I rang the bell; John appeared, he looked very pale.

'What's the matter, John?'

'Sir, my young mistress is crying upstairs ready to break her heart. Hannah was coming downstairs, and heard her say to herself, "Oh, Edward, Edward! I could have borne anything but this, this is too, too cruel!" '

'Just go up, my good man, and tell her luncheon's ready.'

Poor old John! He gave me a look – such a look – and away he went.

Presently he returned.

'Mrs S— will be down directly, sir.'

In a few minutes my lady stalked into the room; there was no trace of tears on her face, she looked like one of the Furies; in the tips of her delicate fingers, in the very tips, and as if she thought them polluted by the contact, she held out to me a remarkably pretty little lace cap, ornamented with a cherry-coloured ribband. The cap was white and clean as driven snow, yet had it been filthy and full of vermin, she could not have regarded it with greater disgust. There was a storm brewing, that was evident, so I became as calm as possible. That is a peculiarity of mine.

'Sir!' said she, with a grand air, 'may I be permitted to enquire how this cap came in your bed?'

'Yes, madam! you may enquire; sorry I can throw no light on the subject,' and I coolly lit a cigar; she watched me like a tigress about to spring.

'Do you dare, sir, to lie in my face! Whose cap is this?'

'Perhaps,' said I, stopping to pull at my cigar, for it did not draw well, 'perhaps it is Hannah's, you know she might have dropped it when she made the bed yesterday.'

'Hannah's indeed!' she cried, with great contempt. 'No, sir, it is not Hannah's, as you know quite well, but that little slut Emma's! And how came those stains on the bed, sir? answer me that.'

'Really, my dear madam, you are becoming so experienced that I know not how to reply to you. What stains do you allude to. I cannot surely have had a wet dream?'

'Wet dream, you vile, bad, debauched man! I know what they mean very well!' and she flew at me like a panther, and planted such a tremendous box on my right ear as nearly knocked me out of my chair.

I very calmly flung the remainder of my cigar under the grate, and seizing both her wrists with a grip of iron, forced her into an armchair. 'Now you little devil,' said I, 'you sit down there, and I give you my honour I will hold you thus till you abjectly and most humbly beg for mercy, and ask my pardon for the gross insult you have inflicted upon me.'

'Insult! think of the insult you have put upon me, you vile wretch, to demean yourself with a little low-bred slut like that!' and struggling violently, she bit the backs of my hands until they were covered with blood, and kicked my shins till she barked them.

'I say, my dear,' said I, 'did you ever see Shakespeare's play of *Taming the Shrew*.'

No answer.

'Well, my angel, I'm going to tame you.' She renewed her bites and kicks, and called me all the miscreants and vile scoundrels under the sun. I continued to hold her in a vice of iron. Thus we continued till six o'clock.

'If it is your will and pleasure to expose yourself to the servants,' said I, 'pray do, I have no sort of objection, but I will just observe that John will come in presently to clear away the luncheon and lay the cloth for dinner.' A torrent of abuse was the only answer.

'You brute,' she said, 'you have bruised my wrists black and blue.'

'Look at my hands, my precious angel, and my shins are in still worse condition.'

By and by there was a rap on the door, 'Come in,' said I. John appeared. 'Take no notice of us, John, but attend to your business.'

John cleared away the luncheon, and laid the cloth for dinner. Exit John.

'Oh, Edward, you do hurt my wrists so.'

'My ear and face are still burning with the blow you gave me, my hands are torn to pieces with your tiger teeth and will not be fit to be seen for a month, and as to my shins, my drawers are saturated with blood,' said I.

'Let me go! let me go directly, wretch!' and again she bit, kicked and struggled.

'Listen to me,' said I, 'there are 365 days in the year, but by God! if there were 3,605, I will hold you till you apologise in the manner and way I told you, and even then, I shall punish you likewise for the infamous way you have behaved.' She sulked for another half-hour, but did not bite or kick any more. I never relaxed my grasp, or the sternness of my countenance. My hands were streaming with blood, some of the veins were opened, her lap was full of blood, it was a frightful scene.

At length she said, 'Edward, I humbly ask your pardon for the shameful way I have treated you. I apologise for the blow I gave you, I forgive you for any injury you have done me, I promise to be docile and humble in future, and I beg – I beg,' she sobbed, 'your forgiveness.'

I released her hands, pulled the bell violently, told John to run immediately for Dr Monson (the family physician), and fell fainting on the floor. I had lost nearly a pint of blood from the wounds inflicted by the panther. When I recovered my senses I was lying on the sofa, my hands enveloped in strapping, plaster and bandages, as were also my shins. Emma and my wife knelt at my feet crying, while Monson kept pouring port wine down my throat. 'Could you eat a little,' said he kindly.

' 'Gad, yes,' said I, 'I'm awfully hungry; bring dinner, John.'

They all stared, it was ten o'clock; however dinner was served, though sadly overdone, having been put back three hours. John had only laid covers for two, presuming my wife and I would dine *tête-a-tête*. I told him to bring two more. Monson and my wife raised their eyebrows – 'Doctor, stay and dine with us, call it supper if you like; Emma, I desire you to seat yourself.' She made towards the door. 'Augusta,' said I, addressing my wife, 'persuade Emma to dine with us. I will it.'

'You had better stay,' said my wife, with a sweet smile. Emma hesitated a moment, and then came and sat beside me.

It was a capital dinner, although damaged, and we all did justice to it. When the cloth was removed, and John had put some port on the table (my mother never gave anything but port and sherry), I proposed a toast, 'Here's to the man who knows how to tame a shrew!' The doctor and Emma looked rather blank, my wife cast down her eyes. 'A bumper! a bumper!' said I, 'I will it.' All three looked at me with some compassion, and filled a bumper and drank it off. At half-past eleven, John brought coffee, after which Monson rose up, and taking my wife aside said in a whisper, which I heard quite well, 'Madam, be careful what you are about; your husband has been shamefully ill-used, and had he died, as I expected he would, you would have been arraigned at a criminal bar for manslaughter. You are a woman of violent passions, learn to restrain them.'

I had one of my bandaged hands up Emma's clothes while he was saying this, and was feeling her lovely young cunny. It was nuts to crack for me.

Dr Monson gone, I rang the bell. 'John, you and the servants can go to bed,' said I. John cast an enquiring glance at Madam and Emma, bowed and retired.

I asked Emma for my cigar-case, as for Augusta, I did not notice her. I lit a cigar, and drawing Emma on my knee, sat before the fire and smoked. 'You can go to bed, Augusta,' said I, as if she was the servant and Emma the wife, 'I shall not want you any more.' The humble woman took her candle, and wishing us both good-night, went to bed.

'Oh, Edward,' said poor little Emma, 'what a dreadful woman she is, she nearly killed you, you nearly bled to death! Dr Monson said two of the great veins at the back of each hand had been opened by her teeth, and that if she had not given in when she did, you would have bled to death.'

'But here I am all alive, my sweet.'

'But you won't have me tonight, mind.'

'Won't I though!'

'Now, Edward! pray don't, you are too weak!'

'Then this will give me strength,' said I, and I drank at a draught a tumbler of Carbonell's old port. I made her drink another glass, and then we lay down on the couch together. I fucked her twice, and then in each other's arms we fell asleep.

It was six o'clock the next morning when I woke up. I aroused Emma, and told her I thought she had better go to her own room, before the servants were about; my hands were very painful, so arranging with her when and where she should next meet me, I went upstairs to bed. My wife was fast asleep. I held the candle close to the bed and looked at her; she was lying on her back, her hands thrown over her head. She looked so beautiful, and her large firm breasts rose and fell so voluptuously, that I began to be penetrated with some sentiments of remorse for my infidelities. I crept into bed, and lay down beside her. I soon fell asleep. I might have slumbered some two hours. I was aroused by being kissed very lovingly. I was sensible that a pair of milky arms clasped me, and that a heaving breast was pressed to mine. I soon became aware of something more than this, which was going on under the bedclothes. I opened my eyes and fixed them upon the ravisher! It was Augusta. She blushed at being caught, but did not release me. I remained passive in her arms. My hands I had lost the use of. Inflammation had set in in the night, I felt very feverish, in an hour more I was delirious; I became alarmingly ill.

I pass over that illness; suffice it to say I kept my bed a month, having the best of all nurses, a mother. As for my wife, she was very zealous at first, but after a week she wearied, and went out of town on a visit to her mother. My mother was very angry at this, but I did not blame Augusta for going, she was young and a sickroom is a dull place.

There was one thing they both agreed in, however, and that was that I should see Emma no more; the opportunity was therefore taken, during my delirium, to send her off to an aunt somewhere in Shropshire, I believe, but wherever it was, I never saw the dear girl again.

I slowly recovered, and then it was arranged that we should go to Hastings for a month. Lodgings there having been taken, my wife rejoined us in town, and to Hastings we went. I soon recovered my usual strength and spirits, and nothing could be more amiable and charming than Augusta, who seemed determined to spare no pains to make me entirely her own. Pursuant to this resolution, she even became amiable to my mother, never contradicting her and yielding in everything.

Peace having been thus happily restored, there seemed every probability of things going well, when an affair occurred which effectually destroyed these alluring prospects.

We were walking one day on the sands when we were passed and repassed several times by a very handsome couple, who were promenading likewise. The lady I recognised at once, but pretended not to know her. She was in fact the little discarded *chère amie* of the suburban villa before alluded to. Each time she passed me she bowed with a bold, confidential air, but finding I was resolved not to know her, she grew angry. 'Jack, old fellar!'

she cried to her young friend, 'do me the favour to knock that man's hat into the water – he has insulted me.' This was said sufficiently loud for us to hear. My wife's eyes flashed fire; she surveyed her *ci-devant* rival from head to foot with a gesture of such indescribable *hauteur* and ineffable disdain that poor little Jessy was cowed in an instant, and cast her eyes on the sand.

I never admired Augusta so much in my life as at that moment; pity she was my wife; but for that chain I could have loved, could have admired her.

The young man, the companion, a gentlemanly-looking fellow enough, advanced and raised his cane with an evident intention of tipping my hat into the waves. I did not stir, but said quietly, 'My friend, you had better not do it, because if you do, I shall be under the very disagreeable necessity of flinging you in after it!'

At this moment Jessy struck down his stick with her pink parasol, merely saying, 'I thought the gentleman was something more than an old acquaintance of mine, but he seems to have forgotten the intimacy,' and she added, 'and has found a fairer partner!'

'Madam!' said I, lifting my hat for the first time, 'this is my wife!'

Jessy looked positively shocked – disbelieve it, ye virtuous Pharisees, if ye will – Jessy the courtesan, my cast-off mistress, with two big tears in her lovely eyes, bowed her head with a meekness I had never seen her exhibit before, and faintly exclaiming, 'Madam, I humbly ask your pardon,' placed her hand on the arm of her companion, and led him quickly away.

'Well, sir!' said Augusta, turning sharply upon me, 'this is truly a charming *rencontre* for your wife to have. And it was quite as likely to have occurred in Pall Mall, or the Park, as here.'

'Quite as likely,' said I.

'Sir, is there any end to your infidelities, how many more are to be intruded upon my notice?'

'Here's the old leaven working up again to the surface,' thought I, so I answered accordingly, 'That is a question which I extremely regret to say I am unable to answer.'

'Not answer! why you know the difference between right and wrong, I suppose, and as a rational being, can abstain from evil if you choose.'

'My dear angel! don't preach, we are not in church but here on the sands, with nobody but these merry little crabs and periwinkles for a congregation. Now, in the first place, I am not at all sure I do know the difference between good and evil, i.e., what the conventional parsons, and the conventional world, are pleased to call good and evil, and inasmuch as I am, at least I hope so, a rational being, I may for example abstain from you, and think it a good action, while I may idolise another girl, and not deem it a bad thing.'

She looked so wretched that I felt touched. 'Will you allow me to offer an explanation of the late unhappy *rencontre*?'

'Oh, explain as much as you like, a man with such principles can lie at his pleasure.'

'Excuse me, madam, a gentleman cannot lie, at least what I call a gentleman, a man of honour.'

'Man of honour, indeed! You gentlemen and men of honour do not hesitate to seduce women and deceive your own wives, to fight duels and kill your adversaries; men of honour, indeed!'

'Ah,' said I, 'that's not the same thing at all, all's fair in love and war, you know. But I maintain that no real gentleman, a man of birth and education, and properly brought up, can tell a mean, sneaking lie for a mean purpose.'

'As you please, sir, tell your story if you wish to do so.'

'Who, I? not the least in the world; hear the explanation or leave it alone, just as you please.'

'I prefer to hear it.'

'It will take a few words; I kept Jessy before, not after, my marriage and discarded her when I did marry.'

'Why did you not tell me so before?'

'You did not give me the chance.'

I thought this denouement would have mollified her; on the contrary she became taciturn and sulky. Oh, woman, woman! if you did but know your little game better. If you did but know how a kind word, a genial smile, will bring the culprit to your feet; if you did but know how temper and the sulks will drive your *sposo* from you. If you did but know this, how many marriages might be happy, though not 'made in heaven'. But, alas, there is a perversity about wives; like the scorpion, they wound themselves with their own sting, and then exclaim, 'See how shamefully I am treated!' and the kind conventional world adds, 'Amen!'

In fine we parted a second time, and I did what I thought a magnanimous thing. I ordered my agent to pay over to her my entire private fortune, £150 a year. I was laughed at by all my dear friends for my folly.

Then came a series of disasters. Our family solicitors, a firm that had managed the affairs of the family for three generations, turned knaves, and my poor mother was plundered of all her property. She was obliged to dismiss all her servants and send her furniture and carriage to the hammer. A country baronet, a man of fortune, a relative of hers, came to her aid and allowed her a hundred a year, and a small house at Brixton received her and her wrecked fortunes. I took an affecting farewell of my dear parent.

'But what will you do, my poor boy?' said the affectionate creature.

'Earn my living, mother, I hope, and help you,' said I. We parted.

For two years I drove the Cambridge mail, but not under my own name. I made about three hundred a year and have reason to think I was much liked on the road. The adventures of that part of my life alone would form a volume, but as this proposes to be an erotic autobiography, I abstain. The advance of the railway system closed this avenue of my career at last. Then I started some fencing rooms in London. Some time after I had become thus engaged, my wife, I could never learn how, found me out. She called upon me, she was beautiful as ever, there was a scene of course, it ended by my agreeing to live with her again. The gods alone know how many infidelities I had committed since we had parted six years before. She never knew them. I accompanied her to the depths of Hampshire, to a certainly charming cottage she had there in a remote hamlet, not a hundred miles from Winchester. Now, it was an anomaly in her character that she, with all her fanaticism, all her pride, should condescend to a meanness. I thought it paltry, and I told her so frankly on our journey, but she represented to me that she had always spoken of me as her husband, Captain S—, and nothing would do but I must be Captain S—.

'But you know,' said I, 'I resigned the service, and have no claim to the title.'

'You have the claim by courtesy,' she said, 'I know several people who call themselves captain and major, merely because that was their rank when they sold out. So you may set your conscience at rest.' I yielded the point.

The cottage was charming, the garden full of flowers, the poultry yard perfect, the pony chaise *à bijou*, the pony, a rough Welsh one, which required no grooming.

There was an orchard, a meadow, and a little Alderney cow; there was only one servant, a blooming, bouncing, buxom girl of sixteen, who did everything and thought herself 'passing rich on six pounds a year'.

Now let the casuists explain it, I cannot, but the three years I passed in this delightful spot –

> The world forgetting,
> By the world forgot –

were the happiest of my chequered existence.

Augusta would strip naked, place herself in any attitude, let me gamahuche her, would gamahuche in her turn, indulged all my whimsies, followed me about like a faithful dog – obtained good shooting for me in the season, and a good mount if I would hunt. Then the squire showed us every attention; the rector and his wife were profuse in their civilities; I had as many whist parties and dinners as I could desire; and all this time I abstained from the blooming servant-maid; I was faithful for three years.

I! A rake, a man about town, fond of gaiety, of theatres, of variety, of conviviality, say – ye casuists – how was it? But so it was; and, sooth to say, I was very happy; a bold rider, I rode with the foremost; a good shot, I bagged my whack of game; while my anecdotes of Indian *shirkarree* (hunting), and of 'pig sticking', delighted the squire; and here I may observe that it soon got to be pretty well known that I had driven the Cambridge mail, but so far from injuring me, it made me the more sought after; in those days many a swell had 'taken to the road', and the examples of Sir Vincent Cotton, Lord C— and Sir Charles R— were sufficient to prove that a gentleman might do this.

What with an occasional invitation to the mess, to the squire's or to the rectory, what with hunting and shooting and gardening and fishing, I did not find a country life so *triste* as I had expected.

Then Augusta knew how to please me, when she liked; nothing could exceed her cleverness in the art of manipulation; she had large and firm breasts, a small and round waist and most voluptuous development of hips; her hands and arms were well turned and handsome. What gamahuching there was – what blisses celestial – the gods and I alone know. And thus passed three golden years, the happiest in my life. From this dream I was awakened by my wife becoming *enceinte*; from that moment 'a change came o'er the spirit of the dream'. Her whole thoughts were now given up to the 'little stranger' we expected, all day long nothing was to be seen but baby clothes lying about the room; she could talk of nothing but baby – drew off my marital amusements, cooled wonderfully in her manner and finally drove me, as it were, to seek elsewhere for the pleasures I no longer found at home.

When the child was born, matters became worse, everything was neglected for the young usurper.

My comforts all disappeared, and at length I became so disgusted that I left her, and going up to town had a long interview with my relative Lord E—.

The earl seemed to think I had been ill-used, and gave me a cheque on his banker; I took up my quarters at the Old Hummuns in Covent Garden for a week, to reflect on the next step I must take. But as a man cannot sit all day yawning over the paper without getting deucedly hipped, I determined to go to Drury Lane Theatre.

So dining upon the best the house afforded at six, by half-past seven I found myself in a capital seat in front of the dress circle. In those days it was a dress circle, where the ladies always appeared in extremely low dresses, naked arms and diamonds (if they had any), and the men in white waistcoats, neckcloth and gloves, black coat and continuations.

That is all changed now. But to resume. I had not taken my seat more than ten minutes when I became aware that a lady in a side box was examining me with her *lorgnette* with great earnestness. I raised my own and levelled it at the fair creature, whoever she might be, in the private box.

'Yes it is certainly her! no, it cannot be! yes, by Jove! it is Mrs B— herself!' I had not seen her for eleven years. By gaslight, and elegantly dressed as she was, it was not possible at so great a distance to see if time had made any havoc in her charms, but I was pleased to see that her only companion was a beautiful girl of fourteen or fifteen; I bowed with *empressement*, she made a gesture with her hand, I arose and joined her in her private box. There were so many enquiries to make on both sides, that we no longer took any notice of the performance.

After I had narrated my matrimonial escapade – and as many of my adventures as I thought it prudent to tell – she related to me that her husband had been dead about four years; that she was a widow, and intended to remain one; that she had eight hundred a year, and a nice house in Porchester Terrace, Hyde Park; that the young lady was a niece of her husband's, an orphan entirely dependent on her; that she would not disguise from me that she had entertained gentlemen sometimes when they took her fancy, and wound up by inviting me to go and visit her for a month. No invitation could have come so opportune, and I accepted it with all the more pleasure as it proved to me that she still took an interest in her old flame. She had never had any children.

While we were talking we had gradually withdrawn ourselves behind the curtain of the box; I had drawn her on my knee with her clothes up, my right hand was slapping her great bottom, which I rejoiced to find had increased in dimensions and was as hard as ever; with my left I explored the grotto of love, which was only altered by the profusion of silky curls that now entwined themselves like the tendrils of a vine around the face of it.

She was now thirty; when last we parted she was a young wife of nineteen. But having never undergone the pains and wrenches of parturition, and having had but light riding in the arena of Venus – she came to my arms as plump and fresh as a rose; her bubbies, too, were the same lovely snowballs, only, if anything, of greater size and volume than heretofore.

We left the theatre about ten, as we had something better to do than to listen to the comedy. The carriage drove first to the Old Hummuns for my luggage; I paid the bill and accompanied her to Porchester Terrace.

'But,' said I, whispering in her ear, as we rode along, 'how do you manage to conceal your intrigues from your servants?'

'There is a secret communication, my dear friend, between

my bedroom and the room you will occupy, and as Constantia shares my room, they will never suspect anything, will they Con?' she added to the girl, to my very great surprise.

'Oh dear me, no, *ma tante*!' laughed the merry girl, 'do you remember when Jack Clavering of the Guards, came and stayed a week, what fun we used to have, but it was never found out – '

'Hush! chatterbox,' cried Mrs B—.

'It seems to me,' thought I, 'I am in for rather a nice thing – I wonder if she'll let me poke the little one!'

'There is only one thing I must caution you against,' said my fair hostess. 'Take liberties with me only in my room, and keep a guard on your tongue, and on those wicked eyes of yours. I look upon all servants as spies, whom we are necessitated to pay and retain that our domestic wants may be attended to. You know I am an Irishwoman and have a great contempt for your *comme il faut* English society, still there is no occasion recklessly to throw away one's reputation, when a little care would save it. Now, mind, I shall speak of you as my brother; for aught my people are aware, I may have been Miss S— before I married; but here we are I see, we must drop the subject now.'

The carriage stopped, I jumped out, and handed out the ladies, we ascended the steps together, the coachman looking well pleased at getting home two hours sooner than he expected.

We all went into the dining-room.

'George,' said Mrs B— to her footman, 'tell Maria, to place my brother's luggage in the same room Major Clavering occupied. The captain [meaning me], has come up to town unexpectedly,' said she with the most wonderful effrontery.

'Yes, ma'am,' said the man, and exit George.

'Do you eat suppers, my dear friend?' asked my hostess.

'Can't say I care for them,' said I.

'Neither do we, but will you not take something, some negus, with your cigar? come, have a cigar!'

'And make your silk damask curtains smell like a taproom for a month? No! no! I won't smoke here if I know it.'

'But we like it, don't we, Con?'

'Oh! the dear cigars, yes! they're charming,' said Con.

'But I have another reason,' said I.

'Another reason!'

'Yes [lowering my voice], smoking enervates!'

'Then pray don't smoke!' said Mrs B— with an enchanting smile.

We sat over the fire for an hour chatting, and then went to bed.

A staid upper housemaid, of a certain age, very demurely showed me to my boudoir, and to prove to her that I was the pink of propriety, I immediately locked the door. I threw myself into an easy chair before the fire, which, with my slippers, had been most invitingly placed there, and waited – presently I was startled by a scratching at the inside of the door of a large mahogany wardrobe, which stood with its back against the wall which divided Mrs B—'s room from mine. I fixed my eyes on the press with astonishment, then I saw a little note slipped under the door. I ran and seized it in an instant, and read as follows:

Undress yourself and put on your nightdress and *robe de chambre* only; in about ten minutes we will let you in – burn this at once.

I put the paper in the fire, and undressed accordingly.

At the appointed time the wardrobe door opened, and the charming smiling face of little Constantia appeared; she had nothing on save her lace nightdress, and her lovely blonde hair hung down her back long below her waist, in wavy locks of gold; she laid her finger on her lips to enjoin silence, and beckoned.

I entered the wardrobe, the door of which she immediately

locked, and when she touched a secret spring in the panel at the back, it sank gradually down into the floor, displaying the interior of another wardrobe, in the next room, the door of which stood open; the next minute I was clasped in the arms of Mrs B—. An argand lamp cast a voluptuous light over the sumptuous chamber, while a bright fire rendered it warm and pleasant. She was quite naked and ready for action, we threw ourselves on the bed, while little Con sat at the foot of it to see the fun. The novelty of the situation aroused all my energies, the idea that that pretty young girl was looking at us fired my senses, and to work we went in right good style; no part of either of us was concealed from the little girl, who at length got so excited that she began manipulating my balls, and feeling the great cock with her little hand as it went in and out.

Then her aunt begged she would come and stride over her that she might gamahuche her, and that at the same time I might behold the beauties of her dimpled bottom. Little Con obeyed with alacrity, but the annexed engraving will convey a better idea than words of the luxury of the attitude.

All that man ever enjoyed with woman, all that poets ever imagined, I realised at that moment. To see the red tongue of that beautiful woman dividing and opening the little coral pouting nether mouth of the sweet young girl, to have all her youthful perfections thus spread out before me was in itself an enchanting treat – but to enjoy at the same time the ripe charms of her aunt, to feel her bounding buttocks bang against my thighs, to slap and toy with her nakedness and feel her spend, I was in the seventh heaven.

As to my pretty hostess, she seemed almost beside herself with delight. She opened wide her mouth, and tried hard to grasp with her lips the entire cunny of the young girl. She forced up her tongue its entire length. She caressed me with her hands, she entwined her legs and then threw them wantonly about.

She bounded and spent; ye gods! how she spent. As for little

Con, she was quite as demonstrative; she jutted out her pretty person, wriggled, grasped the pillows and bed curtains and kept saying, 'Oh, it's so nice! Ah! I do like it so very much. Ah, oh! ah!' and she yielded up her dew from the petals of her lovely rose. Then my partner's climax and mine both came together. I hugged her closer in my embrace, I buried my face in those white hemispheres of the beauteous little Con, and so sent a copious shower into the garden of delight beneath.

After about five minutes respite, I was again primed; this time I had Mrs B— *en levrette*, while her niece lay on a pillow for me to gamahuche her. This was also a delicious fuck.

Then nothing would do, but I must poke little Con while Mrs B— contemplated the scene. I found it was not the first time the little filly had been served.

She was very tight, notwithstanding her little cunny had been well lubricated by the salacious tongue of Mrs B—.

The young girl backed up extremely well. I pressed my face to her exquisite little pointed breasts, I clasped her lovely little bottom – what new and delightful pleasures I experienced. Her cunny had a wonderful contractile power, such as I had never before experienced with woman or girl, and seemed, as it were, to nibble you and draw you in. The darling girl covered me with kisses, and hugged me tight, saying, in a sort of smothered, subdued voice. 'Oh! it is so nice, dear, I do like it so,' etc.

I am afraid I must confess that at that moment I was so rude as to forget that Mrs B— was in the room, I would infinitely rather have had the young girl alone for the rest of the night. But that could not be; my fair hostess had fasted for some weeks, and only flung me the little girl by way of incentive. She no sooner saw that we had finished, than she claimed her rights, and what's more, she got them too. I was at that time about four- or five-and-thirty, in the prime of life, in fact.

My invitation to pass a month ended in my staying three. I must admit it was not all sugar though, for on one or two

occasions Mrs B— (my sister that is!) gave me a taste of her temper; it seemed I was too partial to little Con, and twice I had to vacate my room for a rival. But then on one occasion that rival was the Duke of D—, and on the other, Lord George P—, so, of course, I could not complain.

At length I was fairly fucked out, and could do no more execution. Then, that dear Mrs B—, with that enchanting smile of hers, informed me that the Duke had sent her a superb diamond bracelet, and had given her a cheque for a cool thousand. The latter she insisted on presenting to me, as she did not want the money. 'Adieu, my dear friend,' said she, 'you can now go to Baden-Baden, and drink the waters for a year, at the end of which time, return my old acquaintance, and if you are restored to vigour, you will find me the same.'

Thus we parted. Now what shall I say? The saints and hypocrites who will read this will exclaim, 'What a miscreant this man is.' Read thus far, did I say? Oh! fie! do saints and hypocrites read naughty books? Aye! marry do they, and go home and frig themselves, the beasts, or b—r their footmen. Don't abuse me, you blasted humbugs, members of the Society for the Suppression of Vice! forsooth! Look at home, most worthy religious people! How long is it since one of your Reverend Members was collared by a bobby for assaulting a common, dirty porter boy in the urinal of a railway station, and sentenced to penal servitude for life? Answer me that? A clergyman of the Established Church, too! fie, fie! Gentlemen, I leave such illicit pleasures to the clergy; as for me, I'm a mere fuckster. I like women, and I have them. Go along, you damned, old sodomitical b—rs, and have your boys; but in common honesty, leave honest men to fuck their women in peace, and be damned to you!

'There you go again,' says some captious fellow, who is reading this veritable history, 'digressing again. Damn your old eyes, mind your fucking!'

'It's all very well, sir,' say I, 'but please to consider the tyranny of these people. And all they want is to turn a penny; damn them, they live by their virtue, such as it is.'

Pardon me, gentle, fair, or angry reader, whichever you be, for this digression, but I am a man of spirit, and bite when I'm trod upon. To resume:

And whose fault was it, that I committed these adulteries? Surely my wife's. Had I not been faithful to her for three years! had I not let slip many chances during that time? Venus, thou art a goddess, thou knowest all things! Say how many divine creatures I neglected during that time? for though buried in the depths of the New Forest –

> Full many a flower (there) is born to blush unseen,
>> And waste its sweetness on the desert air.

So saith the poet, and true it is.

And the baby she idolised and loved so well, he grew into boyhood, and she spoiled him, and he grew to man's estate, and became a curse and a disappointment. Go to! now ye fond mothers, who drive your children. What profit have ye? Go to, I say.

But in six months this woman began to feel certain motions of nature, which told her there were other joys besides the pleasure of spoiling her breasts to give suck to her brat, and she wanted to see her *sposo* again. She was virtuous was this woman, so ought to have been 'a crown to her husband'. God knows it has been 'a crown of thorns', but let that pass.

She came up to town, and called on the earl. She was all pathos and meekness, of course. She told her 'sad tale'. My relative was moved, a 'woman in tears' is more eloquent with some people, than 'the woman in white'! I received from my relative a very peremptory letter. I had some expectations from this man; it would not do to offend him; I consented to live with her again.

I smothered my resentment at being coerced into the reunion, and with her I went back to Hampshire, but my erotic readers would only feel bored with a narrative of the family squabbles which ensued, so I pass on to more interesting events.

About a mile from our cottage, was a handsome house surrounded by extensive pleasure grounds. This house was occupied by two ladies, who kept an establishment for young ladies. The front of the premises faced the road, while the plantation at the back abutted on an extensive rabbit warren, the property of my friend, the squire.

One day, having nothing better to do, I took my gun and, whistling to my dogs, sallied out to see if I could knock over a rabbit or two. I was creeping along the quickset hedge, which was a very high one, when I became aware that some of the merry girls were diverting themselves with a swing, and not being aware that one of the masculine gender was so near, made no scruple, in mere frolic, as it seemed, to show their dainty legs, and something more!

In those days drawers had not come generally into fashion and for one girl that wore them, ten did not. I thus had an unrestrained view, and the sight had such an effect on me, that I was obliged to pull out my truncheon to cool him in the summer breeze. I could see them very plainly through the hedge, but whether they could see me, remained to be ascertained. They had not yet chanced to look at the hedge.

Presently, one of them, a pretty little love of about thirteen, said, 'I want to pee!' and holding up her clothes behind, so as to give me full view of her plump white bottom, she squatted down over some stinging nettles, close to the hedge, and performed a very natural libation. The other girls laughed, and told her to 'take care she did not hurt her bottom'. Then the little lady jumped up, and pressing her hand over her clothes between her legs, as I divined to dry certain rosy lips, turned around to see how she had refreshed the stinging nettles. At that moment one of my dogs sneezed, the little girl raised her eyes, and in a moment beheld me from head to foot; my truncheon hard and erect, stood bolt upright, his mushroom-shaped head distended to an enormous size, while I, pretending to be doing what she had just done, stood quite immovable and affected not to see her at all. She stepped softly back to her companions, there was a good deal of whispering and the next instant the swing was deserted and the hedge lined with pretty, eager, blushing faces, like roses on a tree. They one and all looked with all their eyes, and I took care that they should not be balked. Dear little loves, if they wished to gratify their curiosity, why should they not? Now be it observed that I am the last man in the world who would intrude an obscene object before the eye of innocence and modesty; it would be something more than ill-bred and ungentlemanly, it would be cruel – and I am not cruel. I hate cruelty, whether a girl, or a poor cat is the victim, and the other day, taking a short cut through some of the back slums of Seven Dials, I found some young urchins grievously tormenting poor puss. Whereupon I raised my stick and sent the rascals to the right-about, and lifting the poor little animal in my arms, I took her home to my lodgings, fed her, and retained her with me. Whenever I come home, poor puss comes up to me, purrs a welcome, arches up her back and rubs herself against my legs. She is grateful, and knows her protector, and I am rewarded. Now if I would not tolerate cruelty to so mean a creature as a cat, be sure I would not wilfully be cruel to a young girl. But these girls were evidently neither innocent nor modest. Ergo, I let them look their fill. At length they drew off, so I, taking up my gun, began popping at the rabbits. In about half an hour I had bagged three, so thinking that enough, I thought of going home. I was now at the other side of the plantation, where was a wall, for fruit trees I concluded; it was not very high, but sufficiently so to conceal me. I heard laughter and voices on the other side of this wall, and listened. It was the girls talking over their adventure.

'Well, there is one thing certain,' said one, 'he did not see us, and did not know we were looking at him.'

'Oh! that is evident,' said another, 'if he had seen us he would have gone away.'

'What a handsome man he was,' said a third, 'I hope I may get such a husband.'

'Yes,' said a fourth, 'and what a funny great thing it is! I wonder whether all men are like that. I'm sure my little slit would never let it in.'

I was highly entertained with this chat, and longed to be amongst them, but it will never do to force matters, so I went home with my rabbits, and thought the matter over. How could I manage to get admitted within the sacred precincts?

After what the girls had said among themselves, it was plain there could be no ill consequences from the past adventure.

I therefore went boldly up to the house the next day, and sent in my card. I was asked into the drawing-room, and the ladies of the establishment appeared. I had expected to see a pair of shrivelled old maids. Imagine my surprise at beholding in the sisters a lovely woman of thirty, a widow, and a sweet creature of about five-and-twenty.

'Really,' said I, 'I feel I have taken an unwarrantable liberty by this intrusion, but I am an enthusiastic gardener [!], and I heard that your grounds were laid out with such exquisite taste – a taste all your own, I am fully aware – that I was most desirous to see them; then I am very fond of a good romp with children, and I flatter myself I can render myself agreeable to your young people.'

'I assure you, Captain S—, we are highly honoured by this visit. It has always been a source of regret to my sister and myself that we were unacquainted with Mrs S— and yourself. My poor husband was an officer in the Indian army, and Indian men are very acceptable society to me, and I have heard so much from the squire and from our worthy rector in your favour that I am delighted, I am sure, to become known to you,' said the pretty widow.

'Alas! madam,' said I, 'it would give me sincere pleasure to see my wife a little more sociable with her neighbours, but I will tell you *entre nous*, that she always conceives an antipathy for those who like me! She is so clever, too, that she generally manages to create a coolness between my friends and myself before long, and hence, whenever I meet with a more charming acquaintance than usual, I studiously avoid introducing her.' The sisters exchanged glances. 'Ah!' said I, pathetically, 'you have heard as much.'

'We had,' said they in a breath, 'moreover, that she has not a good temper.'

'I am always grieved,' said I, 'to admit the faults of the absent, but it is a fact. I deplore it much, but if you will permit me to visit your charming retreat sometimes, I shall feel proud of the honour you do me, I'm sure.'

It was about half-past one. 'This is the hour,' said the widow, 'that our pupils generally dine, and we take our luncheon; if you will favour us with your company at lunch, we shall be most pleased, Captain S——, and as you are fond of a romp, we will give the children a half-holiday, and you shall be master of the revels, if you will.'

Nothing could suit my book better, so I accepted at once.

No sooner did we enter the luncheon room, than every eye was fixed upon me; they recognised me at once, and deep were the blushes on the fair maiden cheeks. 'Girls,' said the widow, 'this is Captain S——, a gentleman of good family, and a friend of my landlord, the squire, and of our worthy rector. He is very fond of young people, and will show you several new games this afternoon, and has obtained a half-holiday for you.' All eyes were turned upon me, and their expression was all I could wish. The girls got very merry over their dinner, and we over our luncheon, and I managed so to ingratiate myself with my fair hostesses, that they pressed me to stay to dinner, and to pass the evening.

'It will give me the greatest pleasure,' said I, 'but permit me to write a line to my wife, to tell her not to wait dinner.'

'By all means,' said the sisters.

'Your gardener's boy can take it, I presume,' I continued.

'Oh yes,' said the sisters, 'Dick shall take it.'

I wrote as follows –

My dearest Love – I am going to dine at the mess of the —th tonight; give the bearer my dress coat, a clean white waistcoat and my black trousers and varnished boots; put a clean handkerchief in the pocket of the coat, and give it a dose of Jean Maria Farina! I shall be home by half-past twelve.

Your faithful Sposo,

E. S—

'May I be permitted to give my injunctions to the messenger,' said I.

'Certainly,' said the widow, and she rang the bell. A servant appeared. 'Tell Dick to come up to the house directly,' she said.

Presently the same servant announced that Dick was in the hall. I went down. I eyed the lad from head to foot. 'Come out here into the garden,' said I. He was a bright, sharp boy. 'Now, my lad, look here, you know Carysfort Cottage?' said I.

'Yes, sir.'

'You go there and deliver this note; if any of the servants or my wife asks you any questions, you will say that you came from the barracks at Winchester, mind, and that Captain S— (that's me you know) is going to dine there, and you will bring back a leathern bag with you here.'

'All right, sir,' said the lad, with a knowing look.

'You'll do, my lad,' said I, 'here's half a sov. for you.'

The boy looked first at the little bit of gold, and then at me.

'You don't mean I'm to keep this, captain?'

'Yes, be 'gad! that's for your trouble.'

'Dang it,' said Dick, 'you be a genelman, and no mistake. All right, yer honour!'

This affair settled, I returned to the luncheon room.

'Now my dear Captain S—,' said the sisters, 'you'll excuse us accompanying you now. We are obliged to maintain a strict discipline, and the girls would not enjoy themselves half as much if we were present at the sports you are going to introduce them to; we shall therefore hope to have you all to ourselves this evening.'

I was so entirely of their opinion that I did not press the matter; and the young ladies and I sallied out together.

The swing was the first object of attraction for me, and to the swing we went.

'I'll show you how to swing my pets,' said I, and picking upon the prettiest girl among them, a charming blonde of twelve, 'Will you have a swing, my dear?' I exclaimed.

'I shall be delighted,' said the little creature.

I lifted her up to put her in, and in doing so managed to get my hand under all her clothes. She blushed, but made no opposition, so I had a good feel, and arranging her clothes so that everything would be shown, I commenced swinging her; every time she went high in air, I had an enchanting view.

At first there was a little affectation of modesty amongst them, but as I frigged them into the swing, one after another, the laughter and fun became universal. At length I proposed swinging with one of them in my lap, and took the opportunity to get into the one selected; at first she turned her blushing face towards me, and hid it in my bosom; but becoming animated with pleasure, she threw all restraint aside, flung out her legs and opened wide her thighs, so that all could see upon what sort of a pommel she was riding.

The girls surrounded us, they studied every movement, they frigged themselves and each other; they relished it immensely.

Suddenly one of them whispered, 'There's somebody coming!' so down went their clothes in an instant. I had no time to get out of my charmer, even if I had been inclined to, and contented myself with knowing that her muslin frock concealed both her and me. The gardener merely came with his mistress's compliments, and she hoped the young ladies were not getting too boisterous for me.

'Oh, dear me!' said I, 'say, with my compliments, if you please, that I am as much a child as any of them, and that we are all very happy!'

The gardener laughed and went away.

The swinging went on gaily, and ere many minutes our climax came. Most delightful was the novelty of the whole romp, and I do believe I might have had them all if I liked; but, unfortunately, just then the rope broke, and down we came to the ground. I was a good deal shaken, but I saved the girl from getting hurt

We therefore now ran into the wood for a game at hide and seek; but, lo! just as we had all dispersed to find the hider, who should I behold coming down one of the avenues but – my wife!

I doubted not but she had found out everything, and plunged headlong into the wood; at length I reached a hedge, squeezed myself through an opening in it, and ran home at full speed.

There would be a scene of course, but I felt it was better it should take place at my house than before so many witnesses. Nothing could have been more unlucky, as it completely spoiled our sport.

I will not inflict on the reader an account of the row that ensued. Suffice to say that the boy Dick, clever as I thought him, went and told his father the injunctions I had given him about my being at Winchester. He also showed the old man the present I had made him. The gardener was a married man with

daughters as well as sons. He saw me swinging with one of the young ladies in my lap (happily, he saw no more), and the rascal then went and told Augusta all he had learnt and seen.

She immediately divined the whole plot, and hence her sudden appearance on the festive scene. As to the ladies who kept the school, she rated them in no measured terms for their imprudence in allowing a rake like me such licence.

After this escapade, I could no longer remain in Hampshire, so packed my portmanteau, and was once more a gentleman at large in London.

One day I was going down Regent Street, when I met . . .

(The narrative here abruptly terminates, and as far as it has been possible to ascertain, it would appear that the writer died shortly after; at all events he was never seen alive again by any of his numerous acquaintance. – Ed.)

∽§ *Glossary* §∾

argand lamp	a lamp with a tubular wick that admits a current of air inside as well as outside the flame
b—r	bugger; anal intercourse
comme il faut	conforming to accepted social usage; proper
cove	companion
Don Pedro	the pretender to the throne of Portugal at the time of Sellon's narrative, living in Brazil
empressement	emotional interest or involvement
enceinte	pregnant
en levrette	from behind; literally 'like dogs'
en règle	steadily; in the ordinary way
gamahuch(e)	oral sex
griffin(s)	newcomer(s)
hipped	depressed, worried or hypochondriac
loo	a card game popular at the time
mail	mail coach
matutinal	occurring in the morning
mauvaise honte	bashfulness; shyness
negus	a beverage of claret, port or other wine, heated with hot water, sweetened and

	often flavoured with lemon juice and nutmeg
otium cum dignitate	ease with dignity
palankeen	a travelling carriage
piçe	one sixty-fourth of a rupee; a small amount of money
press	a closet or cupboard
quickset hedge	a hedge or thicket planted for ornamentation or as a boundary marker and typically made up of English hawthorn
S—	Sellon
sauve qui peut	'let him save himself, who can'
sov.	sovereign, an English gold coin
sposo	spouse
stingo	a strong liquor, specifically Humming Ale
tante mieux	so much the better

❦ *Postscript* ❧

Captain Edward Sellon's 'erotic autobiography' ends quite suddenly, in mid-sentence to be exact. The original publisher, William Dugdale, appended a note indicating that the author died soon after penning the specific episode left unfinished. A careful chronology of Sellon's life indicates that more likely than not the author killed himself within a few weeks of writing the last words found in his manuscript.

Thanks to Henry Spencer Ashbee, the indefatigable chronicler of Victorian pornography, we have one final chapter to Sellon's picaresque life. It is in the form of a letter, dated 4 March 1866, sent most likely to Ashbee himself. The date is just one month prior to Sellon's suicide, and was written at a time when Sellon had already decided that he would take his own life. Where a lesser man in the same circumstances might author a contrition, so that the world would think better of him, Sellon remains constant, frank and unrepentant. He almost relishes the libertinism of his conduct.

Here, in his own words, is the final written chapter of Captain Edward Sellon's erotic life. (The following text is taken from the letter as reprinted by Ashbee in his *Index Librorum Prohibitorum*, London, 1877, pp. 393–6.)

London, 4th March 1866

MY DEAR SIR – You will be very much surprised no doubt to find that I am again in England. But there are so many romances in real life that you will perhaps not be so much astonished at what I am going to relate after all.

You must know then that in our trip to the continent (Egypt it appears was a hoax of which I was to be the victim) we were to be accompanied by a lady! I did not name this [lady] to you at the time, because I was the confidant of my friend.

On Monday evening I sat for a mortal hour in his brougham near the Wandsworth Road Railway Station waiting for the 'fair but frail', who had done me the honour to send me a beautiful little pink note, charmingly scented with violets, in which the dear creature begged me to be punctual – and most punctual I was I assure you, but alas! she kept me waiting a whole hour, during which I smoked no end of cigars.

At length she appeared; imagine my surprise! I, who had expected some swell mot or other, soon found myself seated beside the most beautiful young lady I ever beheld, so young that I could not help exclaiming, 'Why, my dear, you are a mere baby! how old may I be permitted to ask?' She gave me a box on the ear, exclaiming, 'Baby indeed! do you know, sir, I am fifteen!' 'And you love Mr Scarsdale very much, I suppose?' said I as a feeler. 'Oh! *comme ça!*' she rejoined. 'Is he going to marry you at Vienna, or Egypt?' I asked. 'Who's talking of Egypt?' said she. 'Why I am I hope, my dear, our dear friend invited me to accompany him up to the third Cataract, and this part of the affair, you I mean, my dear, never transpired till half an hour before I got that pretty little note of yours.' 'Stuff!' she said, 'he was laughing at you; we go no farther than Vienna!' 'Good!' said I, 'all's fair in love and war,' and I gave her a kiss! She made no resistance, so I thrust my hand up her clothes without more ado. 'Who are you, my dear?' I enquired. 'The daughter of a merchant in the city who lives at Clapham,' said she. 'Does your mother know you're out?' I ejaculated. 'I am coming out next summer,' said she. 'That is to say you were coming out next summer,' said I. 'Well I shall be married then you know,' said the innocent. 'Stuff!' said I in my turn. 'How stuff?' she asked angrily, 'do you know he has seduced me?' 'No my angel, I did not know it, but I thought as much – but don't be deceived, a man of Mr Scarsdale's birth won't marry a little cit like you.' She burst into tears. I was silent. 'Have you known him long?' she asked. 'Some years,' said I. 'And you really think he won't marry me?' 'Sure of it, my dear child.' 'Very well, I'll be revenged; look here, I like you!' 'Do you though! by Jove!' 'Yes, and – ' I give you my word I was into her in a moment! What bliss it was! None who have not entered the seventh heaven can fathom it! But alas we drew near the station, and I only got one poke complete. She pressed my hand as I helped her out of the brougham at the Chatham and Dover Station, as much as to say 'you shall have me again'. Scarsdale was there to receive her. Not to be tedious, off we started by the mail and duly reached Calais, off again by train. Damned a chance did I get till we were within ten or twelve verses of Vienna. Then my dear friend fell asleep, God bless him! The two devils of passengers who had travelled with us all the way from Calais had alighted at the last station – here was a chance!! We lost not an instant. She sat in my lap, her stern towards me! God! what a fuck it was! 'See Rome and die!' said I in a rapture. This over we were having what I call a straddle fuck, when lo! Scarsdale woke up! I made a desperate effort to throw her on the opposite seat, but it was no go, he had seen us. A row, of course, ensued, and we pitched into one another with hearty goodwill. He called me a rascal for tampering with his fiancée, I called him a scoundrel for seducing so young a girl! and we arrived at Vienna! 'Damn it,' said I as I got out of the train with my lip cut and nose bleeding, 'here's a cursed piece of business.' As for Scarsdale who had received from me a pretty black eye, he drove off with the sulky fair to a hotel in the Leopoldstadt, while I found a more humble one in the Graben near St Stephen's Cathedral, determined, as I had £15 in my pocket, to stay a few days and see all I could. But as you will find in Murray a better account of what I did see than I can give you, I will not trouble you with it. I got a nice little note the next day from the fair Julia appointing a meeting the next day at the Volksgarten. How she eluded the vigilance of her gallant I don't know, but there she was, sure enough, in a cab, and devilish nice cabs they are in this city of Vienna, I can tell you. So we had a farewell poke and arranged for a rendezvous in England, and the next day I started and here I am, having spent all my money!

So there's the finish of my tour up the Nile to the third Cataract, to Nubia, Abu Simbel, etc. It is very wrong I know. I deplore it! but you also know that what's bred in the bone, etc., so adieu, and believe me

Yours very truly,

E. SELLON

Perhaps enough, or too much, has been said of this unique Victorian scallywag, a man of many talents and too few good goals to apply them to. Yet everyone deserves an epitaph, and Sellon was kind enough to provide one for himself, a short poem entitled 'No More'. Although this piece was first published in *Cythera's Hymnal* in 1870, it was perhaps the last piece he ever wrote, and was supposed to have been sent to his mistress at the time of his death.

❧ *No More!* ❧

*Vivat lingam. Non resurgam.**

No more shall mine arms entwine
Those beauteous charms of thine,
Or the ambrosial nectar sip
Of that delicious coral lip –
                No more.

No more shall those heavenly charms
Fill the vacuum of these arms;
No more embraces, wanton kisses,
Nor life, nor love, Venus blisses –
                No more.

The glance of love, the heaving breast
To my bosom so fondly prest,
The rapturous sigh, the amorous pant,
I shall look for, long for, want –
                No more.

For I am in the cold earth laid,
In the tomb of blood I've made.
Mine eyes are glassy, cold and dim,
Adieu my love, and think of him –
                No more.

* Freely translated from the Latin as: Long live erection, for I'll not rise again.

Wordsworth Classic Erotica